GCSE
PHYSICS

Michael Shepherd
Head of Science
Malvern College, Worcestershire

EDUCATIONAL

Every effort has been made to trace copyright holders and to obtain their permission for the use of copyright material. The authors and publishers will gladly receive information enabling them to rectify any error or omission in subsequent editions.

First published 1979
Revised 1981, 1983, 1986, 1987, 1989, 1994
Reprinted 1988, 1991, 1993, 1995, 1996

Letts Educational
Aldine House
Aldine Place
London W12 8AW
0181 740 2266

Text: © Michael Shepherd 1994
Design and illustrations: © BPP (Letts Educational) Ltd 1994

British Library Cataloguing in Publication Data
A CIP record for this book is available from the British Library.

ISBN 1 85758 310 8

Printed in Great Britain by W M Print Limited, Walsall, West Midlands WS2 9NE

Letts Educational is the trading name of BPP (Letts Educational) Ltd

Preface

This book will help you prepare and revise for GCSE and SCE examinations in Physics. It differs from a conventional text book in that the subject matter consists of a detailed but concisely expressed account of Physics in the form most suitable for revision. A further feature of this book is the inclusion of a large number of diagrams, for so much of Physics which is difficult to explain in words can be clearly shown in pictures.

This book commences with vital information about your examination, and advice on studying and revising, examination technique and coursework. Each of the following 26 chapters then covers an important area of Physics and ends with a summary of the vital points. After the chapters is a self-test section containing many multiple choice questions. These are designed to enable you to judge your progress and the answers are provided. Finally, there is large selection of multiple choice, short answer and structured examination questions, most of which are taken from the sample assessment materials provided by the Examining Groups. Specimen answers are given.

Since the first GCSE edition of this book was published in 1987, significant changes have taken place with the introduction of the National Curriculum. In this edition much of the text has been revised, new chapters have been added on the Earth and its Atmosphere and the Earth's Place in the Universe, and the question sections have been replaced completely.

I am grateful to the following Examining Groups for permission to reproduce some of their sample assessment material:

Midland Examining Group (MEG)
Northern Examinations and Assessment Board (NEAB)
Northern Ireland Council for the Curriculum Examinations and Assessment (NICCEA)
Scottish Examination Board (SEB)
Southern Examining Group (SEG)
University of London Examinations and Assessment Council (ULEAC)
Welsh Joint Education Committee (WJEC)

The answers given are my own and in no way the responsibility of the Examining Groups.

Finally I would like to thank the staff of Letts Educational for their advice, encouragement and unfailing courtesy.

Michael Shepherd 1994

Contents

Introduction

Knowing how to prepare for an examination can be difficult. This book will make it easier by providing you with a revision course. It contains not only the necessary topics, but also has a self-test section and an extensive selection of sample examination questions with answers. To get the best from the study scheme in this book you are advised to follow the procedure outlined below.

How to use this book

Turn to pages 3–9 for the Analysis of Examinations. This book covers all GCSE and Scottish Physics syllabuses. Find the Examining Group, the syllabus and the tier applicable to your Physics course and examinations (if you are not sure ask your teacher). The Analysis of Examinations shows you:

- which levels correspond to your tier.
- the number of examination papers you will have to take and their length.
- the percentage of the total mark awarded to the external examination and to internal teacher assessment.
- the types of questions used in the examination papers.
- the address of your Examining Group. You may wish to contact the Group for past examination papers or a copy of the syllabus.

The table on pages 7–9 relates the contents of this book to the National Curriculum levels for GCSE and shows which topics are applicable to the Standard Grade in Scotland and the International GCSE. For GCSE you should concentrate on the National Curriculum levels which correspond to the tier for which you are entered. A '●' in the column for your syllabus indicates that knowledge of that topic is required, if your examination tier includes the level shown on the left. Examination papers will assess mainly the knowledge, understanding and skills specified in the levels appropriate to each tier. They will assume that candidates have a grasp of the knowledge, understanding and skills at lower levels.

You are advised to work through as many of the required chapters as possible. You may find it helpful to consult your Examining Group's syllabus as it may give valuable additional information as to what you need to know.

When you feel that you have mastered as many chapters as you can, you should test what you have learned. A self-test section consisting of multiple choice questions has been included to enable you to judge your progress. If you fail to get some of these right, go back to the appropriate chapter and revise more thoroughly. Then test yourself again.

A large selection of sample examination questions has been included to give you maximum practice in answering all types of questions. For convenience these questions have been grouped by type and then subdivided by the chapters to which they relate.

The National Curriculum and GCSE

The National Curriculum deals with the period of compulsory education between the ages of 5 and 16 in four Key Stages. At the end of each Key Stage (at ages 7, 11, 14 and 16) specified subjects are tested. At the end of Key Stage 4 (KS 4) at age 16, assessment is made through the General Certificate of Secondary Education (GCSE).

The GCSE is administered by groups of Examining Boards. There are four groups in England (London, Midland, Northern and Southern), one in Wales and one in Northern Ireland. Different arrangements apply in Scotland (see page 6).

In Physics, as in other subjects, the Examining Groups offer assessment at three levels. The highest tier is intended for candidates who are attempting to gain grades A★, A and B, the middle tier for those aiming for grades C and D and the lowest tier for those who are likely to gain grades E, F and G. The following table shows how National Curriculum levels will be converted to GCSE grades for your final result. You will notice especially that there is no direct correlation between grades C, D and E and levels 7 and 6.

Grade	Level
A*	10
A	9
B	8
C	7
D	7
E	6
F	5
G	4

For all Physics syllabuses in the GCSE examination, 25% of the marks are awarded by teacher assessment of practical work carried out during the two years of the course (except NICCEA which is 24%). This takes the form of periodic assessment by your teacher of a number of pieces of practical work of an investigative nature.

The GCSE examination places emphasis on understanding topics in the syllabus as well as memorizing information. The examination papers are designed to measure positive achievement, which means they are designed to find out what you know and understand rather than what you do not. Fifteen percent of marks in the examination are for the industrial, economic and social applications of Physics.

Spelling, punctuation and grammar

On all written papers, apart from multiple choice papers, and on coursework a mark has to be added for the quality of your spelling, punctuation and grammar. The mark for the written paper will be added by the examiner who marks your paper. Your teacher will add the mark for coursework and this mark will be checked externally by somebody outside your school. Up to 5% of the total mark can be added for spelling, punctuation and grammar. The following advice may help you gain these marks.

Correct spelling, especially of scientific words, is important. As you carry out your revision it is wise to make a list of scientific words and learn the spellings. Words like separate, apparatus, fluorine, neutral, environment and tectonics are frequently misspelt.

Many examination papers do not require you to write in complete sentences. Unless it specifically asks you to write in complete sentences, there should be no penalty for the good candidate who writes the answer in note form. Most papers have opportunities for extended writing. Ensure, if you write in sentences, that the sentences start with a capital letter and finish with a full stop. Keep your sentences simple.

When you have written a sentence or series of sentences read the sentence(s) slowly to yourself. Does it sound right to you? Be careful with the following pairs of words:

its	it's
their	there
has	as

Analysis of examinations

Find your examining group and syllabus in the following tables. This will then give you details of the papers you will have to sit, such as their length and the type of questions set. N.B. All examinations include structured questions involving some extended prose responses.

The actual details of the topics from this book that you will need to study for your syllabus are given in the table on pages 7–9.

Midland Examining Group (MEG)

Address: 1 Hills Road, Cambridge CB1 2EU

Physics 1782

Tiers	Basic	Central	Further
Levels available	3–7	5–9	7–10
Paper numbers	1	2	3
Time in hours	1½	2	2¼
% of overall assessment	75	75	75
Types of questions:			
Short answers	✓	✓	
Structured	✓	✓	✓
Teacher (internal) assessment of coursework (%)	25	25	25

Physics (Nuffield) 1787

Tiers	Basic	Central	Further
Levels available	3–7	5–9	7–10
Paper numbers	1	2	3
Time in hours	1½	2	2¼
% of overall assessment	75	75	75
Types of questions:			
Short answers	✓		
Structured	✓	✓	✓
Teacher (internal) assessment of coursework (%)	25	25	25

Physics (Salters) 1792

Tiers	Basic	Central	Further
Levels available	3–7	5–9	7–10
Paper numbers	1	2	3
Time in hours	1½	2	2¼
% of overall assessment	75	75	75
Types of questions:			
Multiple choice	✓		
Short answers	✓	✓	✓
Structured	✓	✓	✓
Teacher (internal) assessment of coursework (%)	25	25	25

Northern Examinations and Assessment Board (NEAB)
Welsh Joint Education Committee (WJEC)

Addresses: NEAB, 12 Harter Street, Manchester M1 6HL
WJEC, 245 Western Avenue, Cardiff CF5 2YX

Tiers	P	Q	R
Levels available	3–6	5–8	7–10
Paper numbers	P	Q	R
Time in hours	1½	2	2½
% of overall assessment	75	75	75
Types of questions:			
Short answers	✓		
Structured	✓	✓	✓
Teacher (internal) assessment of coursework (%)	25	25	25

Northern Ireland Council for the Curriculum Examinations and Assessment (NICCEA)

Address: Beechill House, 42 Beechill Road, Belfast BT8 4RS

Tiers	P		Q		R	
Levels available	3–6		5–8		7–10	
Paper numbers	1	2	1	2	1	2
Time in hours	1	1½	1	1½	1½	1½
% of overall assessment	30	46	30	46	38	38
Types of questions:						
Multiple choice	✓		✓			
Short answers	✓		✓			
Structured	✓		✓		✓	
Longer					✓	
Teacher (internal) assessment of coursework (%)	24		24		24	

Southern Examining Group (SEG)

Address: Stag Hill House, Guildford, GU2 5XJ

Tiers	Foundation	Intermediate	Higher
Levels available	3–7	5–9	7–10
Paper numbers	2 5	3 6	4 7
Time in hours	1½ 1	1½ 1	1½ 1
% of overall assessment	50 25	50 25	50 25
Types of questions:			
Structured	✓	✓	✓
Teacher (internal) assessment of coursework (%)	25	25	25

University of London Examinations and Assessment Council (ULEAC)

Address: Stewart House, 32 Russell Square, London WC1B 5DN

Physics A

Tiers	Foundation	Intermediate	Higher
Levels available	3–7	5–9	7–10
Paper numbers	2F 3F	2I 3I	2H 3H
Time in hours	1½ 1	1½ 1	1½ 1
% of overall assessment	45 30	45 30	45 30
Types of questions:			
Short answers	✓	✓	✓
Structured	✓	✓	✓
Teacher (internal) assessment of coursework (%)	25	25	25

Physics B

Tiers	Foundation	Intermediate	Higher
Levels available	3–7	5–9	7–10
Paper numbers	2F 3F	2I 3I	2H 3H
Time in hours	1½ 1	1½ 1	1½ 1
% of overall assessment	45 30	45 30	45 30
Types of questions:			
Multiple choice	✓	✓	✓
Structured	✓	✓	✓
Teacher (internal) assessment of coursework (%)	25	25	25

Scottish Examination Board (SEB)

Address: Ironmills Road, Dalkeith, Midlothian EH22 1LE

The Scottish Standard Grade is not part of the National Curriculum that covers England, Wales and N. Ireland, but the topics needed for it are still covered in this book (see SEB column on pages 7–9).

Candidates can take papers at both General and Credit levels or at just one. If both levels are taken, the candidate will be awarded the better of the two grades.

The grade will be awarded on a scale of 5–1, with grade 1 denoting the highest performance. Grade 5 will be awarded when General level has just been missed. Grade 7 indicates that none of the components has been completed.

There will be one paper for each level. The paper will consist of short answer, structured and extended answer (essay-type) questions.

The syllabus is divided into three equal elements:
>
> Knowledge and Understanding
> Problem Solving
> Practical Abilities – These are assessed within the school or college.

A grade is awarded for each of these three elements on the certificate, along with an overall grade.

Tiers	General	Credit
Grades	3–5	1–2
Paper number	1	1
Time in hours	1½	1¾
% of overall assessment	67	67
Types of questions:		
Short answers	✓	✓
Structured	✓	✓
Teacher (internal) assessment of coursework (%)	33	33

International General Certificate of Secondary Education (IGCSE)

Address: University of Cambridge Local Examinations Syndicate, 1 Hills Road, Cambridge, England CB1 2EU

This is a syllabus based upon GCSE used in various parts of the world.

Tiers	Core		Extended	
Grades available	C – G		A – E	
Paper numbers	1	2	2	3
Time in hours	¾	1	1	1¼
% of overall assessment	40	40	40	40
Types of questions:				
Multiple choice	✓			
Structured and short answer	✓		✓	
Structured and free response				✓
Teacher assessment of coursework, or practical test (1 hr), or written test on lab procedures (1 hr) (%)	20		20	

N.B. The topics given in the table on pages 7–9 are for both the core **and** extended curriculums.

Table of analysis of syllabus content

Chapter	Level		MEG	MEG Nuffield	MEG Salters	NEAB WJEC	SEG	ULEAC A	ULEAC B	NICCEA	SEB	IGCSE
1	Intro.	Measurements	•	•	•	•	•	•	•	•	•	•
2.1	6	Speed	•	•	•	•	•	•	•	•	•	•
2.2	8	Velocity	•	•	•	•	•	•	•	•	•	•
2.3	8	Acceleration	•	•	•	•	•	•	•	•	•	•
2.4	9	Uniformly accelerated motion		•		•	•			•	•	•
2.5	9	Distance travelled				•						•
2.6	8	Projectiles		•	•		•	•	•		•	•
3.1	5,8	Newton's Laws of Motion	•	•	•	•	•	•	•	•	•	•
3.2	5	Measuring force	•	•	•	•	•	•	•	•	•	•
3.3	8	The acceleration produced by a force	•	•	•	•	•	•	•	•	•	•
3.4	6,9	Weight	•	•	•	•	•	•	•	•	•	•
3.5	8,10	Motion in a circle	•		•		•	•	•	•		•
3.6	10	Momentum	•	•	•	•	•	•	•	•	•	•
3.7	10	Action and reaction	•		•	•	•	•	•	•	•	•
3.8	6,7	Work	•		•	•	•	•	•	•		•
3.9	4,6	Energy	•	•	•	•	•	•	•	•	•	•
3.10	5,9	Potential energy	•	•	•	•	•	•	•	•	•	•
3.11	5,9	Kinetic energy	•	•	•	•	•	•	•	•	•	•
3.12	7	Power	•	•	•	•	•	•	•	•	•	•
3.13	5	Scalar and vector quantities		•			•	•	•			•
4.1	7	Experiments to study moments	•	•	•	•	•	•	•	•		•
4.2	7	Centre of mass	•	•	•	•		•	•	•		•
4.3	8	Location of the centre of mass	•		•				•	•		•
4.4	7	Stability				•		•				•
4.5	7	Work done by a machine: efficiency	•			•		•	•	•		•
4.6	6	The lever		•		•	•			•		
4.7	7	Pulleys				•		•		•		
5	7	Density	•	•	•	•	•			•		•
5.1	7	Density measurements					•					•
5.2	7	Flotation				•				•		•
6	6	Pressure	•	•		•	•	•	•	•		•
6.1	6	Pressure in a liquid or gas	•		•	•		•	•			•
6.2	7	Atmospheric pressure	•	•	•	•	•	•	•			•
7.1	6,9	Elasticity	•	•	•	•	•		•	•		•
8.1	6	Atoms and molecules	•	•	•	•	•	•	•			•
8.2	6,7	The states of matter	•	•	•	•	•	•	•			•
8.3	7	Brownian motion	•			•	•					•
8.4	7	Diffusion	•			•	•	•	•			•
9.1	5	Solids				•						•
9.2	5	Liquids				•						•
9.3	5	Thermometers				•						•
10.1	7	Boyle's law		•	•	•	•	•				•
10.2	7	Charles' law		•	•	•	•	•				•
10.3	7	Pressure law		•	•	•	•	•				•
10.4	7,9	The universal gas law	•	•	•	•	•	•	•			•
10.5	7	Models of a gas		•	•	•	•	•	•			•

Chapter	Level		MEG	MEG Nuffield	MEG Salters	NEAB WJEC	SEG	ULEAC A	ULEAC B	NICCEA	SEB	IGCSE
11	8	Specific heat capacity	•	•		•	•	•	•		•	•
11.1	8	Specific heat capacity of a solid	•				•	•	•		•	•
11.2	8	Specific heat capacity of a liquid	•				•	•	•		•	•
12.1	7	Conduction	•	•	•	•	•	•	•	•	•	
12.2	7	Comparison of thermal conductivities			•	•	•	•	•	•	•	•
12.3	7	Radiation	•	•	•	•	•	•	•	•	•	•
12.4	7	Convection	•	•	•	•	•	•	•	•	•	•
12.5	7	Preventing heat transfer	•	•	•	•	•	•	•	•	•	•
13.1	5,8	Progressive waves	•	•	•	•	•	•	•	•	•	•
13.2	8,10	The ripple tank	•	•			•	•	•	•	•	•
13.3	5	Reflection	•	•	•		•	•	•	•	•	•
13.4	7	Refraction	•	•	•	•	•	•	•	•	•	•
13.5	10	Interference	•	•	•	•	•	•	•	•		
13.6	10	Diffraction	•	•	•	•	•	•	•	•	•	•
14.1	5	Rectilinear propagation (light)	•	•	•	•	•	•	•	•	•	•
14.2	5	Reflection at a plane surface	•	•	•	•	•	•	•	•	•	•
15.1	7	Refraction at a plane boundary	•	•	•	•	•		•	•	•	•
15.2	5	Internal reflection and critical angle	•		•	•	•		•		•	•
15.3	5,6	Refraction at a spherical boundary			•	•			•	•	•	•
15.4	7	The focal length of a converging lens							•	•	•	•
15.5	7	Construction of ray diagrams	•		•	•	•		•	•	•	•
15.6	8	Simple microscope			•	•			•		•	•
15.7	8	The camera	•		•	•			•	•		•
15.8	4,5	The eye	•		•	•			•	•	•	
16.1	10	Diffraction (light)	•	•	•	•	•	•	•	•		•
16.2	10	Interference (light)	•	•	•	•	•	•	•			
16.3	10	Polarization (light)	•	•	•	•	•	•	•	•		
16.4	8,9	The electromagnetic spectrum	•	•	•	•	•	•	•	•	•	•
17	5,8	Sound	•	•	•	•	•	•	•	•	•	•
17.1	3,6	Echoes	•	•	•	•	•	•	•	•	•	•
17.2	6	Pitch	•	•	•	•	•	•	•			•
17.3	6	Intensity and loudness	•	•	•	•	•	•	•			•
17.4	6	Quality	•		•	•		•				
17.5	8	Resonance	•		•	•	•		•			
18	4	Magnets				•						•
18.1	6	Making magnets				•						•
18.2	6	Magnetic fields				•						•
19	8	Electrostatics	•	•	•	•	•	•	•	•		•
20	6,9	Current electricity	•	•	•	•	•	•	•	•	•	•
20.1	6	Potential difference	•	•	•	•	•	•	•	•	•	•
20.2	6	Resistance	•	•	•	•	•	•	•	•	•	•
20.3	4	Ammeters and voltmeters	•	•	•	•	•	•	•	•	•	•
20.4	4,6	Resistors	•	•	•	•	•	•	•	•	•	•
20.5	4,6	Resistors in series	•		•	•		•	•	•	•	•
20.6	4,6	Resistors in parallel	•		•	•	•		•	•	•	•
20.7	5,9	Energy (electricity)	•	•	•	•	•	•	•	•	•	•
20.8	4,9	Power (electricity)	•	•	•	•	•	•	•	•	•	•
20.9	4	Cost (electricity)		•	•	•	•	•	•	•		
20.10	7	House electrical insulation	•		•		•		•	•	•	•
20.11	8	Circuit breakers			•	•	•				•	•
20.12	6	Fuses	•		•	•	•	•	•	•	•	•
20.13	6	Earthing	•		•	•	•	•		•	•	•

Chapter	Level		MEG	MEG Nuffield	MEG Salters	NEAB WJEC	SEG	ULEAC A	ULEAC B	NICCEA	SEB	IGCSE
21	7	Electromagnetism	•	•	•	•	•	•	•	•	•	•
21.1	7	The electromagnet	•	•	•	•	•	•		•		•
21.2	8	The microphone		•	•							•
21.3	8	The loudspeaker	•	•	•	•		•			•	•
21.4	7	Force on charges moving in a magnetic field	•	•	•	•	•	•	•	•	•	•
21.5	7	The d.c. electric motor	•	•	•	•	•	•	•	•	•	•
22.1	10	Laws of electromagnetic induction	•	•		•	•	•	•	•	•	•
22.2	7	The d.c. dynamo				•		•		•		•
22.3	10	The a.c. dynamo	•	•	•			•	•		•	•
22.4	10	The transformer	•	•	•	•	•	•	•	•	•	•
22.5	10	Power transmission	•	•	•	•	•	•	•	•	•	•
23.1	10	Thermionic emission	•	•	•		•	•			•	•
23.2	6	The diode		•	•	•	•					•
23.3	8	Cathode rays					•				•	•
23.4	8	Effect of electric and magnetic fields	•	•				•			•	•
23.5	8	Cathode ray oscilloscope	•	•				•			•	•
23.6	5	Semiconductor materials	•	•	•	•	•	•	•		•	•
23.7	5	The p–n junction diode			•	•		•	•			•
23.8	5	The light emitting diode	•	•	•	•	•	•	•		•	•
23.9	5	The transistor			•	•			•		•	•
23.10	5	The bistable	•	•	•		•					
23.11	5	Electronic systems		•	•	•	•			•	•	
23.12	5	Logic gates	•	•	•	•	•	•	•	•	•	
24.1	8	Radiation detectors		•	•	•		•				•
24.2	8	Atomic structure	•	•	•	•	•	•		•	•	•
24.3	8	Isotopes			•	•	•	•				•
24.4	6,9	Radioactivity	•	•	•	•	•	•	•	•	•	•
24.5	8	Uses of radioactivity	•	•	•	•	•	•	•	•	•	•
24.6	9	Radioactive decay	•	•	•	•	•	•	•	•	•	•
24.7	8	Safety (radioactivity)	•	•	•	•	•	•			•	•
24.8	8	Nuclear energy	•		•	•	•	•		•		•
25.1	4	Weathering						•				
25.2	4	How has soil formed?						•				
25.3	6,8	Rocks in the Earth's crust				•		•				
25.4	9	The Earth's structure				•	•	•	•	•		
25.5	9,10	Plate tectonics				•	•	•	•			
25.6	10	The theory of plate tectonics				•		•				
25.7	4,6	Winds, weather and climate	•	•	•	•	•	•	•			
25.8	5,7	The water cycle and weather phenomena	•	•	•	•	•	•	•			
25.9	5	Water supplies	•	•	•	•	•	•	•			
25.10	8	Origins of the Earth and atmosphere	•					•	•	•		
25.11	4,9	Weather maps	•			•	•	•	•			
26.1	Intro.	The Earth and the universe	•	•	•	•	•	•	•	•	•	
26.2	6	What are stars?	•	•	•	•	•	•	•	•	•	
26.3	6	The Sun	•	•	•	•	•	•	•	•	•	
26.4	4	Days, nights and seasons	•	•	•	•	•	•	•	•	•	
26.5	5	Planets and the solar system	•	•	•	•	•	•	•	•	•	
26.6	3,9	Gravity and gravitational forces	•	•	•	•	•	•	•	•	•	
26.7	10	The origin of the solar system	•	•		•	•	•	•	•	•	
26.8	7,9	The Earth and its Moon	•		•	•	•	•	•	•	•	
26.9	9	Our exploration of space		•		•					•	
26.10	10	The life cycle of stars	•		•	•	•	•	•	•		

Revision, exams and coursework

Studying and revising

The best way to ensure a good result in your examination is to make sure that you *understand* the various topics in your course *as you are taught them*. Once a topic is understood, revising it and remembering it are so much easier.

Of course, revision during the last few months leading up to your examination is also very important. Time is precious, so make sure that you use it well. A good method is to devise a revision timetable – make a list of all the topics you have to study and divide up your time accordingly. Be realistic about how much time you will be able to spend on revision.

Revising is, to a great extent, a matter of technique. It is not good enough to simply read through your notes or text book time and time again. There are various methods which you can use to help you revise. No one method in itself is better or worse than another. It really depends on which you find easiest. Here are a few methods for you to consider.

- **Underline or highlight important words and sentences.**
- **Make lists of key words.**
- **Write out important definitions.**
  Writing notes will help you to remember key points.
- **Draw diagrams to summarize important topics.**
  Label the diagrams and write notes at the side. Many people find it easier to remember things from pictures than from words.
- **Summarize important ideas and explanations.**
- **Keep all your notes and diagrams** so that you can look at them again. Diagrams and notes that you have made yourself will jog your memory and your understanding very quickly. Concise and well-organized notes and diagrams will increase your long-term knowledge and understanding significantly.
- **Answer the self-test and sample examination questions** in this book and check the answers. Answering examination questions is one of the best ways to prepare for an examination.
- **Ask your teacher if you still do not understand something.**
  Whichever method of revision you choose, develop it and persevere. A good revision technique can make all the difference to your final examination performance.

Looking after yourself

Keeping fit and well during revision and the examination period is at least as important as making sure that you know and understand your work.

- Do not try to do too much revision. Set aside a realistic time for revision each day and stick to it. If you are intending to work in the evenings, start work as early as possible.
- Study for a short period of about 30–40 minutes, then take a short break of about 10 minutes. Then continue revising for another 30–40 minutes before taking another short break, and so on.
- During breaks try to think of something entirely different from revision. Relax!
- Try to work in a quiet, well-lit, well-ventilated room.
- While revising avoid distractions from family, friends, radio and television.
- Make sure that you have regular meals, that you get enough sleep and that you take regular exercise.
- Do not try to do much revision the evening before an examination. Just quietly read through the brief notes you have already made to reassure yourself.

Types of examination questions

Multiple choice (objective) questions

All questions must be attempted in multiple choice examination papers or sections of examination papers. It is therefore unnecessary and a waste of time to read the paper or section through before starting to write down your answers. However, as you come to each question do read it carefully before answering, as each word in the question is significant. In particular read *all the alternative answers carefully* before deciding on your answer.

Start at question 1 and work steadily through the paper doing all of the questions you can answer fairly easily. Do not delay, at this stage, over questions which you find difficult. Working in this way you should be able to reach the end of the paper or section of the paper in a little over half the time allowed for it, having answered about two-thirds of the questions. Now return to the beginning and tackle the questions you found difficult the first time through, but still leave out the questions about which you have little or no idea. You should aim to reach the end 5 or 10 minutes before your time runs out.

Now is the time to return to the few questions still not answered and make an intelligent guess in each case. Generally you will be able to decide that two or three of the alternative answers to each question are definitely wrong, but you may not be sure which one of those left is correct. If you guess at this stage you will have a one in two, or one in three, chance of being right. However, *wild guessing is useless* and you should not guess at any answers until the last few minutes. *Do not leave any questions unanswered.* Examining Groups do not deduct marks for wrong answers.

If you have any time left after you have answered all of the questions, check through your answers, bearing in mind the following points:

- All questions should have an answer.
- No question should have more than one answer – this can occur by mistake when filling in the sheet.
- Any alteration should be such that the incorrect answer has been completely rubbed out. For this reason, a soft pencil should always be used for completing the answer sheet.

Short and structured questions

In these types of question a space for the answer is normally left on the question paper. If this is the case, the space left is a guide, *but only a guide*, to the length of the answer required. Do not feel that you have to fill the space completely, but if you find your answer is much too short or much too long, think again. Another indication of the length of answer required is the number of marks printed alongside the question or part of the question. One mark often indicates that little more than a one or two word answer is expected. On the other hand, four marks is an indication that an answer of several lines may be necessary.

Whether or not space is left for answers on the question paper, your answer should contain all the *relevant* points, stated in a logical order and concisely expressed.

Coursework

During the GCSE course your teacher will assess your scientific skills in carrying out experimental and investigative work. The investigations include three strands:

1 *Designing investigations, asking questions, predicting and hypothesizing*
In this strand you will be expected to:
  (i)   write down the factors (variables) which might affect a phenomenon (level 4), e.g. the factors which affect the resistance of a piece of wire, such as length, radius (or area) and the material from which it is made.
  (ii) use your scientific knowledge and understanding to predict how the different factors affect the phenomenon (level 5/6), e.g. if the radius (or area) is increased, does the resistance change? If so, does it increase or decrease?
  (iii) predict the relative effect of two or more factors (level 7), e.g. will increasing the length or increasing the radius (or area) have the greatest effect on the value of the resistance?
  (iv) make *quantitative* predictions, plan the investigation and suggest what data you will need to collect (level 8/9), e.g. you might predict that doubling the length of the wire would double its resistance.
  (v)   try to explain the effect of different variables using scientific knowledge and ideas (level 10), e.g. use the idea of atomic motion within the wire to explain electrical resistance and its variation with length or radius (or area).

2 *Carrying out investigations; observing, measuring and manipulating variables*
In this strand you will be expected to:
  (i)   make observations and measurements of the key variables while keeping other possible variables constant (level 4/5), e.g. measure the time of swing (period) of a pendulum for different lengths of string keeping the mass of the pendulum bob and the amplitude or angle of swing constant.
  (ii) investigate the effect of altering two or more variables (level 7), e.g. measure the time of swing of a pendulum for different lengths of string keeping other variables constant; then measure the time of swing for different amplitudes or angles of swing keeping other variables constant.
  (iii) use systematic techniques to judge the relative effects of different factors (level 9), e.g. systematically carry out the experiments suggested in (ii) to enable you to assess the relative effects quantitatively.
  (iv) collect valid and reliable data to enable you to evaluate the idea or phenomenon under consideration (level 10).

3 *Interpreting investigations, drawing conclusions and evaluating evidence*
In this strand you will be expected to:
  (i)   use your observations and results to draw conclusions (level 4).
  (ii) use your results to draw conclusions and state the relationship between variables (level 6), e.g. draw a graph of the time of swing of the pendulum against the length of the string, and conclude that as the length increases so does the time of swing.
  (iii) state the relative effects of different variables (level 7), e.g. draw graphs to show that the time of swing of the pendulum is unaffected by the amplitude or angle of swing, but it increases as the length of the string increases.
  (iv) analyse and interpret your data to show an appreciation of errors and uncertainties (level 9), e.g. give a list of experimental errors and the precautions that you took to make the investigation fair and accurate. If possible, indicate any doubts that you have about your conclusions.

(v) analyse and explain your results in terms of a scientific law, theory or model and try to assess how well it explains your results (level 10).

Your teacher will assess your practical skills by watching how you carry out experiments and by assessing your written report of an experiment or investigation. He or she should assess you on at least two occasions to give you a chance to do well on each of the three strands at least once.

Your written coursework should include the following:

1. A *clear title* and an *introduction* stating what you are investigating.
2. A list of the *factors* (*variables*) you are investigating. Predict the relative effects of at least two factors, making quantitative predictions, if possible.
3. A *diagram* of your apparatus.
4. A *description* of what you will do and the data you will collect.
5. *Tables of your results*, showing the units of all the quantities measured.
6. *Graphs* which enable you to make concise *conclusions* about the effects of different variables. Try to make your conclusions quantitative and compare the relative effects of the different variables.
7. Any *precautions* you take for safety reasons or to make your investigation more accurate.
8. A list of the sources of *error* in your investigation and an indication of *uncertainties* in your conclusions.
9. An explanation of your conclusions in terms of scientific laws, theories and models.

Chapter 1
Measurements

All measurements in Physics are related to the three chosen fundamental quantities of **length**, **mass** and **time**. For many years scientists have agreed to use the metric system; the particular one used now is based on the metre, the kilogram and the second.

1.1 Length

The unit of length is the metre. Various multiples or submultiples are also used. Thus

1 kilometre (km) = 1000 metres (m)

1 metre = 100 centimetres (cm) = 1000 millimetres (mm)

1 centimetre = 10 millimetres

For day-to-day work in laboratories metre and half-metre rules are used – graduated in centimetres and millimetres. For more accurate measurement vernier calipers or a micrometer screw gauge may be used. Details of both these instruments will be found in any standard textbook. A metre rule is accurate to the nearest millimetre, calipers to the nearest 0.1 mm and a micrometer gauge to 0.01 mm.

1.2 Mass

The mass of a body measures the quantity of matter it contains. The unit of mass is the kilogram. A body will have the same mass in all parts of the universe.

1 kilogram (kg) = 1000 grams (g)

1 gram = 1000 milligrams (mg)

1.3 Area and volume

The area of a surface is measured in units of metres times metres (m^2) or cm^2 or mm^2. The volume of a substance is usually expressed in units of m^3 or cm^3 or mm^3.

The volume of a liquid is often measured in litres or millilitres.

1 litre (1) = 1000 millilitres (ml)

but   1 millilitre = 1 cm^3

therefore   1 litre = 1000 cm^3

In Physics the measuring cylinder is most commonly used for volume measurements of liquids. When reading the value it is important to look at the bottom of the curved liquid surface (meniscus).

1.4 Time

The scientific unit of time is the second (s) which is $\dfrac{1}{24 \times 60 \times 60}$ part of the time the Earth takes to perform one revolution on its axis.

In the laboratory, time is normally measured using a stopclock or stopwatch. In some cases more accuracy is required, as, for example, when measuring the acceleration of a trolley moving on a ramp. A tickertape vibrator (also known as a 'ticker timer'), or a centisecond or millisecond timer should then be used. The sensitivities of these four instruments are as follows:

stopwatch or stopclock	1/10 s
tickertape vibrator	1/50 s
centisecond timer	1/100 s
millisecond timer	1/1000 s

In some experiments it may be appropriate to use a stroboscope to measure time. A description of the hand-operated stroboscope and its use is given at the end of Unit 13.2.

Chapter 2
Speed, velocity and acceleration

2.1 Speed

Speed is defined as the distance moved in one second.

$$\text{Average speed} = \frac{\text{distance moved}}{\text{time taken}} \text{ (m/s)}$$

2.2 Velocity

The velocity of a body measures its speed and the direction in which it travels.

$$\text{Average velocity} = \frac{\text{distance moved in a particular direction}}{\text{time taken}}$$

(m/s in a particular direction – north for example)

Uniform velocity means that both the speed and the direction remain constant, as shown in Fig. 2.1(b).

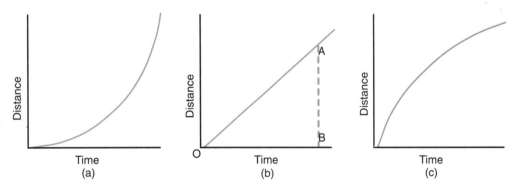

Fig. 2.1 Variation of distance moved in a straight line with time: (a) increasing velocity; (b) uniform velocity; (c) decreasing velocity

In Fig. 2.1(b) *AB* represents the distance travelled in the time represented by *OB*, thus

$$\text{Velocity} = \frac{AB}{OB}; \text{ this is called the slope or gradient of the graph}$$

In Fig. 2.1(a) and (c) the gradients vary. Thus they represent bodies whose velocities have different values at different times.

2.3 Acceleration

If the velocity of a body is changing, the body is said to be accelerating. Acceleration is defined as the change in velocity per second.

$$\textbf{Acceleration} = \frac{\textbf{change in velocity}}{\textbf{time taken for this change}}$$

For example, suppose a car travelling along a straight road increases its speed from 10 m/s to 20 m/s in five seconds.

$$\text{Change in velocity} = (20 - 10) \text{ m/s} = 10 \text{ m/s}$$

$$\text{time taken for this change} = 5 \text{ s}$$

Hence using the formula above:

$$\text{acceleration} = 10 \text{ m/s in } 5 \text{ s} = 2 \text{ m/s in } 1 \text{ s}$$

$$\text{thus acceleration} = 2 \text{ m/s}^2$$

In this example the acceleration resulted from a change in the magnitude of velocity (speed). However, velocity can change in either magnitude or direction (circular motion). A change in either means the body is accelerating.

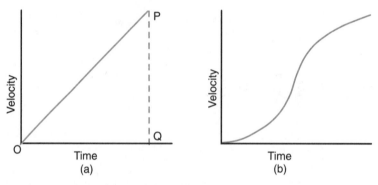

Fig. 2.2 Acceleration: (a) uniform acceleration; (b) non-uniform acceleration

In Fig. 2.2(a) the velocity is increasing with time at a steady rate, and the acceleration is said to be uniform. *PQ* represents the change in velocity in time *OQ*.

$$\text{Acceleration} = \frac{PQ}{OQ} \text{ ; the gradient of the velocity–time graph}$$

In Fig. 2.2(b) the acceleration is not constant. The acceleration at any instant is found by calculating the gradient of the graph at that time.

2.4 Uniformly accelerated motion

The body whose motion is represented by Fig. 2.3 is moving with a velocity *u* when timing starts. It has a **uniform acceleration** of *a* m/s² which means that each second its velocity increases by *a*, and after *t* (seconds) its velocity will have increased by *at*. Hence at the end of this time its velocity *v* = *u* + *at*.

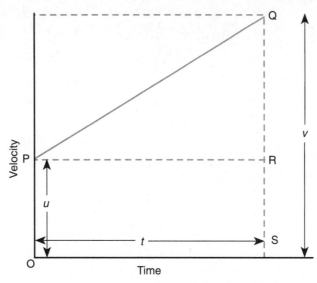

Fig. 2.3

Alternatively, $\qquad$ Acceleration $a = \dfrac{\text{change in velocity}}{\text{time taken for this change}}$

$$= \frac{v - u}{t}$$

therefore $\qquad v - u = at$

and $\qquad \boldsymbol{v = u + at}$ $\qquad\qquad$ (2.1)

2.5 Distance travelled

The average velocity of the body whose motion is shown in Fig. 2.3 is equal to half the sum of its initial velocity u, and final velocity v.

Average velocity $= \dfrac{u + v}{2}$ (this only applies to a body accelerating uniformly)

The distance s moved can be found using the equation:

$$\text{Velocity} = \frac{\text{distance moved}}{\text{time taken}}$$

hence $\qquad$ distance moved = average velocity $\times$ time taken

$$s = \frac{(u + v)}{2} \times t \qquad\qquad (2.2)$$

but $\qquad v = u + at$ $\qquad\qquad$ (2.1)

Therefore $\qquad s = \dfrac{(u + u + at)t}{2}$

or $\qquad \boldsymbol{s = ut + \tfrac{1}{2}at^2}$ $\qquad\qquad$ (2.3)

In Fig. 2.3, ut is the area of the rectangle $OPRS$. The area of the triangle PQR is

$$\text{area } PQR = \tfrac{1}{2} \times \text{base} \times \text{height}$$

$$= \tfrac{1}{2} \times t \times (v - u)$$

but $\qquad v - u = at$ from equation (2.1)

Thus $\qquad$ area $PQR = \tfrac{1}{2}at^2$

Area of $OPQS =$ (area of rectangle $OPRS$) + (area of triangle PQR)

Hence $\qquad$ area of $OPQS = ut + \tfrac{1}{2}at^2$

but $\qquad s = ut + \tfrac{1}{2}at^2$ $\qquad\qquad$ (2.3)

The area under the velocity–time graph in Fig. 2.3 is therefore equal to the distance travelled by the body. This is true for all such graphs, even when the acceleration is non-uniform.

A third equation for uniformly accelerated motion may be obtained by eliminating time t between equations (2.1) and (2.3). The resulting equation is

$$v^2 = u^2 + 2as \qquad\qquad (2.4)$$

2.6 Projectiles

So far we have only considered objects travelling in a straight line. In this unit we shall study objects which are being accelerated by the force due to gravity and at the same time are moving horizontally at a steady speed. One example of such motion is the path of a ball which is projected horizontally over the edge of a table. This ball continues to move with the same horizontal speed as it had just as it left the edge of the table (if we ignore the small effect of air resistance). In addition the ball falls under the influence of gravity.

It can be shown that the ball takes the same time to reach the ground as another ball dropped from the same height at the moment the first ball leaves the edge of the table. This shows that the horizontal motion of the first ball in no way affects its vertical acceleration; that is, it falls in exactly the same way as it would if it were not moving sideways. The horizontal and vertical motions of the ball can be treated entirely separately.

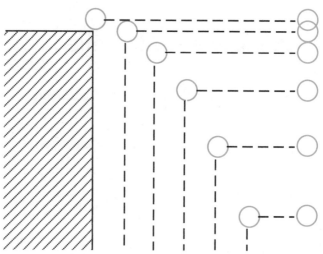

Fig. 2.4 Projectile motion

Figure 2.4 represents the motions of the two balls already mentioned. The paths of the two have been photographed at regular intervals. It can be seen that in equal time intervals both balls fall an increasing but equal distance (they undergo the same vertical acceleration). In the same equal time intervals the first ball moves equal distances horizontally. This motion may also be demonstrated using the pulsed water drops experiment. Another example of projectile motion is that of a ball thrown from one person to another.

Summary

1   **Average speed** $= \dfrac{\textbf{distance moved}}{\textbf{time taken}}$ (m/s)

2   **Average velocity** $= \dfrac{\textbf{distance moved in a particular direction}}{\textbf{time taken}}$

(m/s in a particular direction – north for example)

Velocity is a vector quantity (i.e. it has magnitude **and** direction). It may increase, decrease or remain constant.

3 **Acceleration** $= \dfrac{\textbf{change in velocity}}{\textbf{time taken for this change}}$ (m/s^2)

Acceleration is a vector quantity. It may increase, decrease or remain constant – uniform acceleration.

4 For uniform acceleration, the following equations may be used.

$$v = u + at$$

$$s = \frac{(u + v)}{2}\, t$$

$$s = ut + \tfrac{1}{2}at^2$$

$$v^2 = u^2 + 2as$$

where u is the initial velocity, i.e. at time $t = 0$
v is the velocity at time t
s is the distance travelled
a is the uniform acceleration

5 In projectile motion the horizontal and vertical motions may be treated separately. The horizontal velocity is constant. The vertical acceleration is also constant and equal to that produced by gravity.

Chapter 3
Force, momentum, work, energy and power

3.1 Newton's Laws of Motion

The majority of the work discussed in this chapter can be summarized by Newton's Laws of Motion:

1. **Every object remains at rest or continues to move in a straight line at a constant speed unless acted on by a force.**

2. **When a force does act on an object, the object will accelerate (or decelerate). The value of the acceleration is proportional to the size of the force.**

3. **To every action there is an equal and opposite reaction.**

The word force denotes a push or pull. When an object at rest is acted on by a force it tends to move; if a force acts on an object already in motion it will change its velocity, either by altering its speed or its direction or both.

If an object has no force acting on it, the object will remain at rest or it will continue to move with a constant (steady) velocity.

To summarize, force is that which changes, or tends to change, an object's state of rest or uniform motion in a straight line.

It is the total (net) force acting on the object which is important. For example, when an object is moving there is likely to be friction acting against it. A car will accelerate only if the forward force from its engine is greater than the total frictional forces from its moving parts, such as the axle bearings, and the flow of air over its surface.

The frictional force due to the air flowing over the surface of a car body when it is moving increases greatly as the speed of the car increases. Eventually the force of air friction equals the maximum force that the car's engine can produce and the car can go no faster as the total (net) force on it is now zero.

A free-fall parachutist accelerates for some while after leaving an aircraft. Eventually the force due to the air flowing over the parachutist's body is equal but opposite to his weight

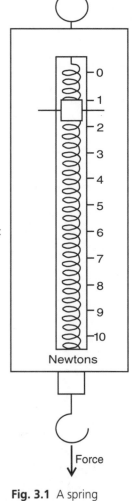

Fig. 3.1 A spring balance for measuring force

and he no longer accelerates. When he opens his parachute the air resistance becomes much greater, due to the large area of the parachute, and he slows down. Eventually, due to his reduced speed, the force of air resistance becomes equal to his weight and he floats to earth at a gentle steady speed.

3.2 Measuring force

A spring balance marked in newtons is suitable for measuring force in a laboratory. The balance consists of a spring whose extension is proportional to the force applied to it. The spring is contained in a case and is calibrated by applying known forces to it, usually in the form of weights (Fig. 3.1).

3.3 The acceleration produced by a force

The relationship between a force and the acceleration it produces can be investigated using a trolley, ramp and ticker-timer (see Fig. 3.2). The ramp has to be raised sufficiently at one end to compensate for friction in the trolley and ticker-timer. The slope should be such that when the trolley with tape in place is nudged, it moves slowly down the ramp at constant speed.

A tape is then obtained by towing the trolley down the ramp with a constant force. This can be provided by either an elastic band stretched a known amount, or by weights hung over a pulley as shown in Fig. 3.2. The experiment is repeated using twice the original force and again using three times the force.

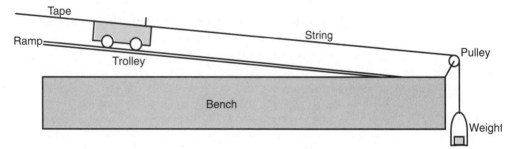

Fig. 3.2

Instead of a ticker-timer a light gate can be used to determine the velocity of the trolley near the end of the ramp. A card 10 cm or 20 cm wide is attached to the trolley so that it prevents the light falling on the photo-transistor while it is passing through the light gate. The time for which the light is cut off is recorded. The velocity of the trolley is found by dividing the width of the card by the time recorded on the electronic timer attached to the light gate. The acceleration of the trolley is calculated by dividing this velocity by the time it took the trolley to reach the light gate, which can be measured using an electronic stopclock.

Histograms can be made if tapes are used. A typical set of results is shown in Fig. 3.3.

Fig. 3.3 (a) Original force; (b) twice the force; (c) three times the force

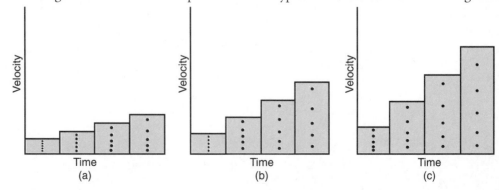

It is clear that if the force doubles, the acceleration doubles, etc., that is

$$\frac{F}{a} \text{ is constant, provided the mass is constant} \tag{3.1}$$

The same apparatus may be used to show how the acceleration *a* depends on the mass *m* of a trolley, when a constant force is used. The force is applied in turn to one, two and three trolleys of similar mass stacked on each other. It is found that if the mass is doubled the acceleration is halved, etc., that is

$$m \times a = \text{a constant} \tag{3.2}$$

The relation

$$F = ma \tag{3.3}$$

will be seen to include both statements (3.1) and (3.2). The unit of force is the **newton (N)** which is defined as the force which gives an acceleration of one metre per second^2 to a mass of one kilogram.

An object which has a large mass requires a large force to accelerate it as can be noted from equation (3.3). Such an object is said to have large inertia; it is difficult to move.

3.4 Weight

The acceleration produced by the Earth when a body is falling freely is written as *g*, which is therefore called the acceleration due to gravity. It is also known as the gravitational field strength. The force on a body due to the Earth's attraction is found by using equation (3.3) which becomes $F = mg$, where *F* is in newtons.

The value of the force acting on a body due to the Earth's attraction is *mg*, or its weight. This force acts downwards, that is towards the centre of the Earth.

The strength of the Moon's attraction is about one seventh of the value of the Earth's attraction. A mass *m* on the Moon's surface would therefore experience a force of only one seventh the value it experiences on the Earth's surface. Its weight on the Moon would be about one seventh of its weight on the Earth.

3.5 Motion in a circle

When a body is moving in a circle its direction of motion, and hence its velocity, is continually changing. A force is needed to achieve this.

If you attach a mass to one end of a length of string, hold the other end and whirl it steadily round in a horizontal circle, you can feel that a force is required to make the mass move in a circular path. The force acts along the string and increases if the mass is whirled faster.

If any object is to move in a circle a force has to be continually applied to the object at right angles to its direction of motion at any instant; that is towards the centre of the circle. This is called the centripetal force. It does not alter the speed of the object, but it does alter its direction of travel and hence its velocity. The force produces an acceleration towards the centre of the circle.

Consider an object of mass *m* moving with a constant speed *v* in a circle of radius *r*. By calculating the rate of change of *velocity*, as the object continually changes direction, the acceleration *a* can be shown to be given by the equation:

$$a = \frac{v^2}{r}$$

but $\qquad F = ma$

thus $\qquad F = \frac{mv^2}{r} \tag{3.4}$

The force required to keep an object moving in the arc of a circle increases greatly as the speed of the object increases. Also it is larger if the radius of the arc is smaller. It is larger for an object of greater mass.

A car or train going round a corner are everyday examples of motion in a circle. Friction between the tyres and the road provides the centripetal force in the case of a car cornering. If the corner is too sharp (r very small), the speed too high, or the road wet, the frictional force may not be large enough to keep the car moving in a circle, and it will slide off the road. The outer rail provides the centripetal force in the case of a train.

Another example of centripetal force is the gravitational force of the Sun on the planets, including the Earth.

3.6 Momentum

A lorry which is fully laden requires a larger force to set it in motion than a similar lorry which is empty. Likewise more powerful brakes are required to stop a heavy goods vehicle than a family car moving with the same speed. The heavier vehicle is said to have more **momentum** than the lighter one. Momentum is a measure of how difficult it is to alter a body's motion; it is more basic even than velocity.

The momentum of a body is defined as the product of its mass and its velocity.

$$\textbf{Momentum = mass} \times \textbf{velocity}$$

Momentum has units of kg m/s.

By studying the linear motion of a trolley down a ramp it has been shown experimentally that the following equation is valid:

$$F = ma$$

but
$$a = \frac{v - u}{t}$$

Thus
$$F = \frac{m(v - u)}{t}$$

so
$$F = \frac{mv - mu}{t} \tag{3.5}$$

or
$$\textbf{\textit{Ft} = \textit{mv} − \textit{mu}} \tag{3.6}$$

Equation (3.5) can be written thus:

$$\textbf{Force} = \frac{\textbf{change of momentum}}{\textbf{time taken for this change}}$$

All the equations just discussed concern momentum change and hence, by the definition of momentum, velocity change. They are therefore valid for changes in the direction of motion of a body as well as for changes in its speed. They apply to circular motion as well as linear, and are summed up in Newton's second law of motion (see Unit 3.1).

3.7 Action and reaction

When two bodies collide the force one exerts on the other is equal in size but opposite in direction to the force the second one exerts on the first. As the time of contact is the same for each, both experience the same change in momentum, but in the opposite direction. The total momentum of the two is thus unaltered by the collision. This is known as **the principle of conservation of linear momentum**. The principle always holds providing no forces, other than those due to the collision, act on the bodies.

This principle can be verified experimentally, for a simple case, using two trolleys and a ticker-timer, on a friction–compensated ramp. Fig. 3.4(a) shows the arrangement.

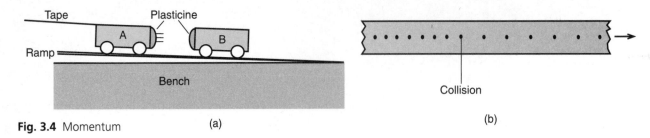

Tape   Plasticine

A   B

Ramp

Bench

Collision

Fig. 3.4 Momentum

(a)

(b)

Some plasticine is placed on the surface of the two trolleys which will come into contact. Drawing pins are embedded in the plasticine on the front of trolley A, and tickertape is attached to the rear of this trolley. Trolley A is given a push so that it travels with a uniform velocity and collides with trolley B. The trolleys stick together and move off with a common velocity. A typical tape is shown in Fig. 3.4(b). The spacing of the dots changes abruptly on collision. The velocity of A before the collision and the combined velocity of the two trolleys after the collision are found from the spacing of the dots. In the experiment the tape is **NOT** being used to show acceleration. Alternatively two light gates may be used, one to determine the velocity of trolley A before collision, the other to determine the combined velocity of the two trolleys after collision. The precise method is described in Unit 3.3. The results show that:

$$\text{Total momentum before collision} = \text{total momentum after collision} \qquad (3.7)$$

Alternatively

$$m_1u_1 + m_2u_2 = m_1v_1 + m_2v_2 \qquad (3.8)$$

where m, u and v represent the masses and velocities of the colliding bodies. In some collisions one of the velocities may be zero or two velocities may have the same value. For example in the experiment just described $u_2 = 0$ and $v_1 = v_2$, as the bodies stick together after collision. Equation (3.8) then becomes simpler.

Suppose that in the above experiment $m_1 = 1$ kg, $m_2 = 3$ kg and $u_1 = 1$ m/s. Then substituting in equation (3.8) we obtain:

$$1 = v_1 + 3v_2$$

but $\qquad v_1 = v_2$

thus $\qquad 1 = 4v_1$

hence $\qquad v_1 = 0.25 \text{ m/s} = v_2$

This is the value we would record from the tape after the collision, thus verifying **the principle of the conservation of momentum**.

The principle of conservation of momentum holds in the case of an explosion as well as a collision. A rocket relies for its propulsion on the fact that it gains a forward momentum equal in size to the momentum of the gases it expels backwards. It will gain forward momentum, and hence increase speed, for as long as it continues to expel these gases.

3.8 Work

The term 'work' is associated with movement. If a railway engine pulls a train along a track with a steady force the work done by the engine depends on the size of the force it provides and the distance it pulls the train with this force. Work is calculated by definition from the relation:

Work done = force × distance moved in the direction of the force

The unit of work is the **joule (J)**. One joule is the work done when a force of one newton moves through a distance of one metre in the direction of the force.

No work is done in circular motion as the force is at right angles to the distance.

3.9 Energy

Anything which is able to do work is said to possess energy. **Energy is the capacity to do work.** All forms of energy are measured in **joules**.

The world we live in provides energy in many different forms, of which chemical energy is perhaps the most important. The use of chemical energy from coal and oil has been a major factor in the development of our civilization. The presence of electricity, light and heat as forms of energy in our homes is something we take for granted. Most of this energy comes from the chemical energy released from coal, oil or gas or from nuclear energy. Coal, oil and gas are fossil fuels and are non-renewable forms of energy.

In the last 30 years there has been considerable research into renewable forms of energy such as energy from the Sun, the wind, the tides and waves.

Solar energy may be harnessed by the use of solar panels on the roofs of buildings. Such panels are black so as to absorb radiant energy from the Sun most efficiently. The energy absorbed normally heats water flowing in pipes just behind the black surface. There are few solar panels in the UK due to the lack of sunshine, particularly in winter. Solar panels are a common sight in tropical countries.

Making use of wind energy involves the building of many large windmills in windy areas, which are often areas of outstanding natural beauty. There are environmental objections as well as economic and engineering problems to be sorted out.

Tidal barriers have been built, the nearest one to the UK being on the Rance estuary, near St. Malo, in Brittany. For many years there have been plans to build a similar one in the Bristol Channel. The engineering problems in producing large quantities of energy economically from wave motion are severe and have not yet been overcome.

Food has chemical energy stored in it, which is released by chemical reaction inside our bodies. Food provides us with energy to keep warm and to do work.

Energy can neither be created nor destroyed, though it may be changed from one form to another. This is a statement of **the law of conservation of energy**.

Although energy may change from one form to another, the second form may not be measurable or useful. Most energy transformations end up with the formation of heat. This is usually spread (dissipated) amongst an extremely large number of molecules and it is not economic to harness it and change it into other types of energy. It is no longer 'useful' energy and can be said to have been 'lost'.

3.10 Potential energy

If a body is to be raised from a bench, an upward vertical force equal to the weight of the body must be provided. Suppose the force applied (mg) raises the body a vertical distance h.

$$\text{Work done} = \text{force} \times \text{distance moved in the direction of the force}$$

Thus $\quad \text{Work done} = mg \times h = \boldsymbol{mgh}$

Once the body has been raised it is said to have increased its **potential energy** by this amount. All the work done has been used to increase the potential energy of the body.

Potential energy is the energy a body has by reason of its position.

3.11 Kinetic energy

If the mass is now allowed to fall it will steadily lose the potential energy it has gained. By the time it has fallen a distance h it will have lost all the potential energy it previously gained. As it falls its velocity increases and it is said to possess an increasing amount of **kinetic energy**. The kinetic energy it has at any instant will equal the potential energy it has lost.

Kinetic energy is the energy a body has by reason of its motion.

As the mass falls it is accelerated by the force of the Earth's attraction on it. Suppose it falls a distance h, in time t, as its velocity increases uniformly from zero to v.

$$\text{Force} = \frac{\text{change in momentum}}{\text{time taken}}$$

Thus

$$F = \frac{mv - 0}{t}$$

and

$$\text{distance} = \text{average velocity} \times \text{time}$$

that is

$$h = \frac{v}{2} \times t$$

$$\text{Work done} = \text{force} \times \text{distance moved in the direction of force}$$

$$= \frac{mv}{t} \times h$$

$$= \frac{mv}{t} \times \frac{vt}{2}$$

$$= \tfrac{1}{2}mv^2$$

The work done by the gravitational force results in an increase of kinetic energy of $\tfrac{1}{2}mv^2$, and a loss of potential energy of mgh.

Suppose a body, mass 5 kg, falls through a vertical distance of 5 m near the Earth's surface where its acceleration due to gravity (g) is 10 m/s^2.

$$\text{Potential energy lost} = mgh = 5 \times 10 \times 5 = 250 \text{ J}$$

$$\text{Kinetic energy gained} = \tfrac{1}{2}mv^2 = 250 \text{ J}$$

$$\text{Thus} \quad \tfrac{1}{2} \times 5 \times v^2 = 250 \text{ J}$$

$$v^2 = 100$$

$$\text{and} \quad v = 10 \text{ m/s}$$

3.12 Power

Power is defined as the work done per second, or the amount of energy transformed per second.

$$\textbf{Average power} = \frac{\textbf{work done}}{\textbf{time taken}} = \frac{\textbf{energy change}}{\textbf{time taken}}$$

It is measured in units of joules per second (J/s). One joule per second is called a **watt (W)**.

$$1 \text{ kilowatt (kW)} = 1000 \text{ watts}$$

A rough estimate of a pupil's power can be made by asking him or her to walk or run up a staircase. If the height of the staircase is measured in metres, the pupil's weight calculated in newtons, and the time taken recorded on a stopwatch, the power can be calculated. The result will normally be about 200 W if walking or 500 W if running.

3.13 Scalar and vector quantities

A **scalar quantity** is one which has only magnitude (size), such as money and number of apples. A **vector quantity** is one which has both magnitude and direction, such as velocity, force and momentum.

Vectors can be represented by straight lines drawn to scale. If a number of forces all act in the same straight line, their resultant is determined by addition or subtraction.

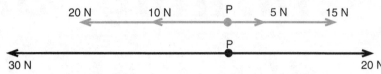

Fig. 3.5

Thus if forces of 20, 15, 10 and 5 newtons all act at a point *P*, as shown in Fig. 3.5, we have:

total force acting towards the left = 10 + 20 = 30 N

total force acting towards the right = 15 + 5 = 20 N

resultant force = 30 − 20 = 10 N acting to the left

Summary

1 When a body is in motion it obeys Newton's laws of motion.

2 The acceleration *a* produced when a mass *m* experiences a force *F* is given by

$$a = \frac{F}{m} \text{ or } F = ma$$

3 When a body of mass *m* moves at constant speed in a circle of radius *r*, the centripetal force *F* is given by

$$F = \frac{mv^2}{r}$$

4 **Momentum = mass × velocity (*mv*)** and is measured in units of kg m/s.

5 The law of conservation of momentum states that when two bodies collide the total momentum in a given direction after collision is equal to the total momentum in the same direction before collision.

6 The change of momentum which occurs when a force acts on a body for a certain time is given by

$$\textbf{Force} = \frac{\textbf{change in momentum}}{\textbf{time taken for this change}}$$

Force is measured in newtons (N).

7 **Work done (or energy transformed) = force × distance moved in the direction of the force.**

8 The change in potential energy (or energy of position) when a mass *m* is moved through a vertical height *h* is given by the equation

Change in potential energy = *mgh*

where *g* is the gravitational field strength.

9 The kinetic energy (or energy of motion) of a mass *m* moving at a velocity *v* is given by

Kinetic energy = $\frac{1}{2}mv^2$

10 Power is the work done per second or the rate at which energy is transformed:

$$\textbf{Average power} = \frac{\textbf{work done}}{\textbf{time taken}} = \frac{\textbf{energy change}}{\textbf{time taken}}$$

11 Energy is measured in joules (J) and power in watts (W). One watt is one joule per second.

12 A **scalar** quantity has only size. A **vector** quantity has size and direction.

Chapter 4
Turning forces and machines

When we open a door, turn on a tap or use a spanner, we exert a **turning force**. Two factors determine the size of the turning effect: the magnitude of the force and the distance of the line of action of the force from the pivot or fulcrum. A large turning effect can be produced with a small force provided the distance from the fulcrum is large. The size of the turning effect is called the **moment**.

The moment of a force about a point is the product of the force and the perpendicular distance of its line of action from the point.

Moment of force = force × perpendicular distance from the pivot

The units of a moment are newton metres (Nm).

4.1 Experiments to study moments

A thin uniform strip of wood, for example a metre rule, is balanced on a fulcrum. A weight is placed on the rule to one side of the fulcrum and a second weight is added on the other side and its position carefully adjusted until balance is restored (Fig. 4.1). Within the limits of experimental error it will be found that:

$$w_1 \times d_1 = w_2 \times d_2$$

Balance can be restored using more than one weight, in which case:

$$w_1 \times d_1 = (w_2 \times d_2) + (w_3 \times d_3)$$

This principle can be extended if further weights are used. When a body is in equilibrium, the sum of the anti-clockwise moments about any point is equal to the sum of the clockwise moments about the same point. The force the fulcrum exerts on the body equals the sum of the weights on the body.

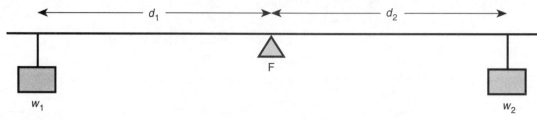

Fig. 4.1 Moments

Suppose, in Fig. 4.1 above, $w_1 = 300$ N, $w_2 = 100$ N, $d_1 = 0.4$ m and $d_2 = 0.5$ m, then we can calculate where a weight of 700 N must be placed to balance the rule.

$$w_1 \times d_1 = (w_2 \times d_2) + (w_3 \times d_3)$$

hence $\qquad 300 \times 0.4 = (100 \times 0.5) + 700d_3$

and $\qquad d_3 = \dfrac{(300 \times 0.4) - (100 \times 0.5)}{700} \text{ m}$

$$= \frac{120 - 50}{700} = 0.1 \text{ m}$$

This weight must be placed 0.1 m to the right of the pivot.

4.2 Centre of mass

The weight of a body is defined as the force with which the Earth attracts it. This says nothing about the point of application of this force. A body may be regarded as made up of a large number of tiny particles, each with the same mass. Each of these particles is pulled towards the Earth with the same force. The Earth's pull on the body thus consists of a large number of equal parallel forces. These can be replaced by a single force which acts through a point called the **centre of mass**.

The centre of mass of a body is defined as the point of application of the resultant force due to the Earth's attraction on the body. Thus we may regard the centre of mass as the point at which the whole weight of the body acts.

4.3 Location of the centre of mass

The centre of mass of a long thin object such as a ruler may be found approximately by balancing it on a straight edge. The same method may also be used for a thin sheet (lamina). In this case it is necessary to balance it in two positions as shown in Fig. 4.2.

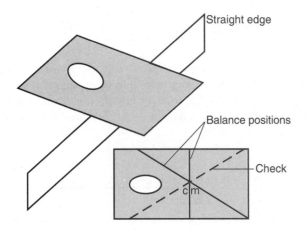

Fig. 4.2 Locating the centre of mass

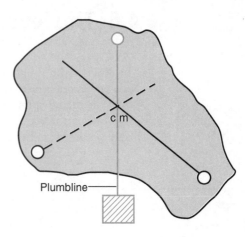

Fig. 4.3

One good way of finding the centre of mass of a lamina is to use a plumbline. Three small holes are made at well spaced intervals round the edge of the lamina, and the lamina and plumbline suspended from each in turn (Fig. 4.3).

The position of the plumbline is marked on the lamina and the point of intersection of these three lines gives the position of the centre of mass.

4.4 Stability

The position of a body's centre of mass affects its stability. For example, the centre of mass of a vehicle should be as low as possible, and its wheel base as wide as possible, if it is to be stable.

When a vehicle corners fast there is a tendency for it to tilt on the outer wheels. It will turn right over when the vertical line through the centre of mass falls outside these wheels. If the conditions stated above are satisfied, the centre of mass has to rise a larger distance for this to happen. This requires more potential energy and it is less likely to occur.

4.5 Work done by a machine: efficiency

A machine is any device by means of which a force (effort) applied at one point can be used to overcome a force (load) at some other point. Most machines, but not all, are designed so that the effort is less than the load. They can be regarded as force multipliers; the force that the effort exerts is multiplied by the machine to be equal to the force that the load exerts.

The ratio of the useful work done by a machine to the total work put into it is called the **efficiency** of the machine. Usually the efficiency is expressed as a percentage.

$$\text{Efficiency} = \frac{\text{work output} \times 100\%}{\text{work input}}$$

In a perfect machine no work would be wasted and the efficiency would be 100%. In practice, work is wasted in overcoming friction and, in the case of pulleys, in raising the lower pulley block. The efficiency is then below 100%.

4.6 The lever

The lever is the simplest form of machine in common use. It can consist of any rigid body pivoted about a fulcrum. Levers are based on the principle of moments discussed earlier in this chapter. A force (effort) is applied at one point on the lever, and this overcomes a force called the load at some other point. Fig. 4.4 illustrates some simple machines based on the lever principle.

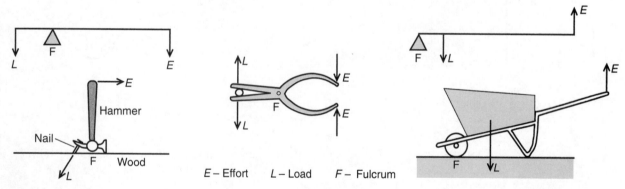

Fig. 4.4 Simple levers

Details of other machines such as the screw jack, inclined plane and gears may be found by reference to standard textbooks.

4.7 Pulleys

A pulley is a wheel with a grooved rim. Often one or more pulleys are mounted together to form a block. The use of pulleys is best illustrated by considering the block and tackle arrangement shown in Fig. 4.5.

For clarity the pulleys are shown on separate axles; in practice the two pulleys in the top block are mounted on a single axle as are those in the bottom block. In order to raise the load by one metre each of the four strings supporting the lower block must be shortened by 1 m. This is achieved by the effort being applied through a distance of 4 m.

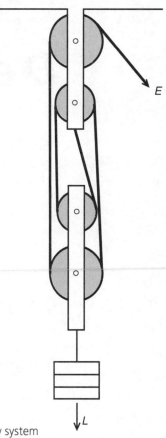

Fig. 4.5 Pulley system

Summary

1   The turning effect of a force about a pivot is called its moment.

   Moment of a force = force × perpendicular distance from the pivot

   It is measured in newton metres (Nm).

2   A machine is any device by which a force (effort) applied at one point can be used to overcome a force (load) at some other point. Most machines are designed so that the effort is less than the load.

   The efficiency of a machine is given by

$$\textbf{Efficiency} = \frac{\textbf{work output} \times \textbf{100\%}}{\textbf{work input}}$$

3   Any lever or pulley system is a type of machine.

Chapter 5
Density

Equal volumes of different substances vary considerably in their mass. For instance aircraft are made chiefly from aluminium alloys which, volume for volume, have a mass half that of steel, but are just as strong. The 'lightness' or 'heaviness' of a material is referred to as **its density**.

$$\textbf{Density} = \frac{\textbf{mass}}{\textbf{volume}} \text{ (kg/m}^3 \text{ or g/cm}^3)$$

5.1 Density measurements

A regular solid

The mass of the solid is found by weighing, either on a chemical balance, if great accuracy is required, or on a spring balance. If the latter is used the result must be converted to mass units; that is if the balance is calibrated in newtons, the value recorded must be divided by 9.81 to obtain the mass in kilograms.

The volume of the solid is obtained by length measurement, using a ruler, vernier calipers or a micrometer screw gauge, depending on the accuracy required. This method is applicable to cuboids, spheres, cylinders and cones amongst other regular shapes. The formulae giving the volume of such shapes in terms of their linear dimensions can be obtained from textbooks. For example, metals are often in the form of turned cylinders whose volume can be calculated from the formula:

$$\text{Volume} = \pi r^2 h$$

where r is the cylinder radius and h is its height.

An irregular solid

The mass is found in the same way as for a regular solid. In order to find the volume it is necessary to partly fill a measuring cylinder with water. The reading is taken and the solid then lowered into the water on the end of a length of cotton, until it is completely immersed, and the new reading taken. The difference between the two readings gives the volume of the solid. This method cannot be used if the solid dissolves in water.

A liquid

A measuring cylinder is first weighed empty using, for example, a top-pan balance. Some of the liquid to be tested is poured into the cylinder, and the cylinder reweighed. The difference between the two readings gives the mass. The volume of the liquid is obtained by direct reading of the measuring cylinder. If a more accurate value is required a specific gravity bottle can be used. Details may be obtained from a textbook.

5.2 Flotation

The density of an object determines whether it sinks or floats. Most types of wood float on water, but steel sinks. Wood is less dense than water, steel is more dense. An object floats on a liquid if it is less dense than the liquid. Geologists use this fact to separate minerals, granite and pitchblende, for example.

When an object is placed in a liquid it experiences an upward force (upthrust) on it. **This upward force is equal to the weight of liquid displaced.** The more of an object there is under the liquid (the more liquid it displaces), the bigger the upward force on it.

When an object floats, its weight is exactly balanced by the upward force (upthrust) of the liquid on it. If the upward force of the liquid on an object is not big enough to balance its weight, even when the object is fully submerged, the object will sink.

A ship floats, despite being made from steel, because it is hollow inside and thus is largely composed of air. Its large volume displaces a weight of water equal to the weight of the ship.

Summary

1   **Density** $= \dfrac{\text{mass}}{\text{volume}}$

It is measured in kg/m^3 or g/cm^3.

2   When an object is placed in a liquid it experiences an upward force which is equal to the weight of liquid displaced.

Chapter 6
Pressure

The word **pressure** has a precise scientific meaning. It is defined as the force acting normally (perpendicularly) per unit area.

$$\text{Pressure} = \frac{\text{force}}{\text{area}}$$

For example, the pressure exerted on the ground by a body depends on the mass of the body and on the area of the body in contact with the ground. A boy wearing ice skates will exert a far greater pressure than if he were wearing shoes. The pressure exerted on the ground by a brick depends on which face is in contact with the ground (Fig. 6.1). However, the weight of the brick and thus the force it exerts on the ground is about 22 N, whichever face is in contact.

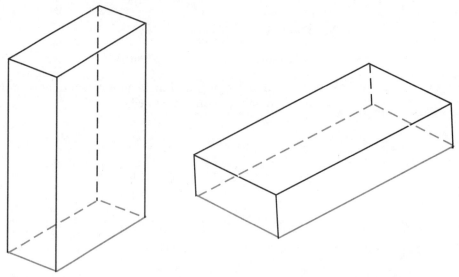

Fig. 6.1

One does not have to use a very large force when using a needle. As the area of the point is very small, a relatively small force produces a large pressure and the needle pierces the material.

6.1 Pressure in a liquid or gas (a fluid)

The pressure in a fluid increases with depth. This may be shown by using a tall vessel full of water with side tubes fitted at various depths (Fig. 6.2).

The speed with which the water spurts out is greatest for the lowest jet, showing that pressure increases with depth. This demonstration also indicates that pressure acts in all directions in a fluid – not just vertically. The pressure responsible for these jets is acting horizontally.

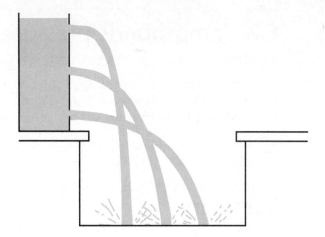

Fig. 6.2

Suppose we consider a horizontal area A at a depth h below the surface of a liquid of density d. Standing on this area is a vertical column of liquid of volume hA, the mass of which is hAd. The weight of this mass is $hAdg$.

$$\text{Pressure} = \frac{\text{force (weight)}}{\text{area}} = \frac{hAdg}{A}$$
$$= hdg$$

The usual units are newtons per metre^2, often called pascals (Pa). The area does not appear in the final expression for pressure in a fluid.

The property of liquids to transmit pressure to all parts is used in many appliances. Some car jacks consist of an oil-filled press used for lifting (Fig. 6.3).

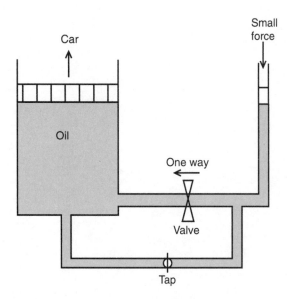

Fig. 6.3 Hydraulic car jack

The pressure exerted on one side of the press is transmitted through the liquid to the other side. Thus a small force applied over a small area on one side can result in a large force over a large area on the other side. A large mass, such as a car, may thus be raised by application of a small force.

Mechanical diggers and bulldozers use hydraulic principles to power the blade or shovel. Cars require a braking system which exerts the same pressure on the brake pads of all four wheels to reduce the risk of skidding. Each brake consists of two brake shoes which are pushed apart by hydraulic pressure in a cylinder and press on the brake drum. When the brakes are applied the increased pressure on the pedal is transmitted through oil to the cylinders in each wheel and the shoes applied.

6.2 Atmospheric pressure

On Earth we are living under a large volume of air. Air has weight and as a result the atmosphere exerts a pressure not only on the Earth's surface but on objects on the Earth. **Atmospheric pressure** is normally expressed in newtons per metre^2 or Pascals. The average value is 100 000 Pa approximately.

Summary

1   The word 'pressure' has a precise meaning.

$$\text{Pressure} = \frac{\text{force}}{\text{area}}$$

It is measured in N/m^2 which is often called a Pascal (Pa).

2   The pressure a distance h below the surface of a liquid which has a density d is

$$\text{pressure} = hdg$$

where g is the gravitational field strength.

3   A pressure applied at one point in a liquid is transmitted to all other points. The brake systems of cars and some car jacks use this principle.

4   The Earth's atmosphere exerts a pressure at the Earth's surface of about 100 000 Pa.

Chapter 7

Forces between molecules in solids

Before materials are used in the construction of machinery, bridges and buildings, tests are carried out to ensure that they are able to stand up to the stresses to which they are likely to be subjected. Brittle substances such as cast iron and masonry will support large forces of compression, but break easily if stretching forces are applied. When stretching forces are likely to be significant, materials such as steel have to be used. The behaviour of a material under the influence of applied forces depends on the forces holding the molecules of the material together.

7.1 Elasticity

Some knowledge of the forces between molecules of a solid can be gained by adding weights to a spiral spring and investigating how it stretches. A spiral spring is suspended vertically from a rigid support and a small pointer attached to its lower end (Fig. 7.1(a)).

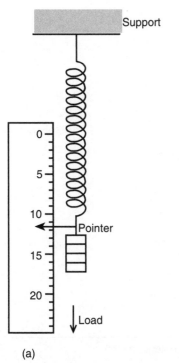

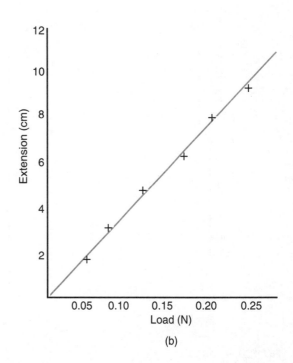

Fig. 7.1　　(a)　　　　　　　　　　　　　　　　　　　　　　　　　　(b)

The reading of the pointer against the scale is noted. Weights are then added in steps to the lower end of the spring and the reading of the pointer recorded after the addition of each weight. The weights are removed in similar steps and a second set of readings taken. For small loads the reading of the pointer should be the same for each set of readings. The average extension for each load is then plotted against the load (Fig. 7.1(b)).

A straight-line graph passing through the origin shows that the extension is directly proportional to the load in the range of loads used; that is, the load/extension ratio is constant. This ratio is called **the spring or force constant.** It is the force required to produce unit (1 cm or 1 m) extension and is normally quoted in units of N/m.

When a small weight is attached to the spring, the spring extends. When the weight is removed the spring returns to its original length. The property of regaining its original size or shape is called **elasticity** – thus putty is a very inelastic material whereas metals regain their original shape and are therefore elastic. In a metal the forces of attraction between the displaced molecules are sufficiently strong to restore the molecules to their original position.

If larger weights had been added to the spring a stage would have been reached when the spring would not have returned to its original shape on removing the weights. The spring is permanently stretched or deformed. Beyond a certain load the molecules do not return to their original positions when the load is removed. The extension at which this occurs is called the **elastic limit** of the spring. With greater loads the molecules are unable to keep their fixed positions in the metal.

The forces between the molecules of a metal can be further investigated by stretching a length of straight wire. A length of wire is suspended vertically from a fixed support and weights added to its lower end, in a similar way to the procedure for a spring. However, the extension of the wire within its elastic region is very small, and if this region is to be studied a more accurate method of measuring extension has to be used. It is usual to use two wires, one carrying a vernier and the other a millimetre scale (Fig. 7.2(a)). The second wire is for comparison purposes and is not stretched. This comparison method of measuring extension eliminates errors due to thermal expansion and sag of the support.

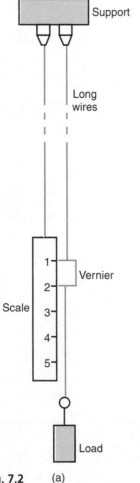
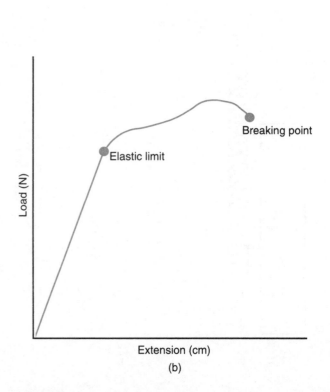

Fig. 7.2   (a)   (b)

The results for a wire (Fig. 7.2(b)) are as for a spring, with a load/extension graph giving a straight line until the elastic limit is reached.

The results from these two experiments may be summarized in what is known as Hooke's law:

The deformation of a material is proportional to the force applied to it, provided the elastic limit is not exceeded.

While stretched the spring or wire has potential energy stored in it. The area under the load/extension graph is equal to this stored energy. If the elastic limit is not exceeded then this energy is released when the spring or wire returns to its original length. If the elastic limit is exceeded then the extra energy stored is used to permanently deform the spring or wire and becomes heat.

Summary

1   An object is said to behave elastically when equal increases in the force applied to it produce equal changes in length. That is, a graph of the force applied against the extension is a straight line through the origin. When this is so Hooke's law is said to be obeyed.

2   The elastic limit is the point beyond which the object no longer behaves elastically.

Chapter 8
Kinetic theory of matter

8.1 Atoms and molecules

In 1808 John Dalton produced experimental evidence to show that chemical compounds consist of molecules. A molecule is a group of atoms. There are about 90 different chemical elements occurring in nature, each of which has its own characteristic atom.

Some idea of the size of molecules can be gained from an experiment to measure the thickness of a very thin oil film. A tank with a large surface area is required for this experiment and the water which is placed in the tank must be very clean. Lycopodium or talcum powder is lightly sprinkled on the water surface. A small oil drop is then placed on the surface of the water near the centre of the tank. It can be transferred to the water using a loop of fine wire or a small syringe. Immediately the oil drop touches the water surface the powder is pushed back by the oil film to form a ring of clear water, the diameter of which is measured.

The oil film may be considered as a cylinder of radius R and height h. Hence its volume $= \pi R^2 h$. The value of h is calculated by equating the volume of the oil film to the volume of the oil drop placed on the water surface. On extremely clean water, olive oil is considered to spread until the film is one molecule thick. In this case h is an estimate of the diameter of an oil molecule. The value obtained is about 2×10^{-9} m.

8.2 The states of matter

The molecules in a solid are each anchored to one position, about which they vibrate continuously, as if held in position by a framework of springs. When heat energy is supplied, thus raising the temperature, the molecules vibrate faster and through greater distances than before. Thus the extra energy is transformed into kinetic energy of the molecules.

If sufficient heat energy is supplied a solid will melt to form a liquid. The amplitude of vibration of the molecules becomes so large that they break away from the position to which they were anchored and move freely amongst each others. However, forces still act between the molecules holding them close to each other, and so although a liquid has no definite shape, it does have a definite volume. The volume of a liquid is much the same as the solid from which it forms, thus the average separations of the molecules are about the same in each case, as are the densities. The molecular separation in the liquid may be slightly greater than in the solid (e.g. wax) or slightly less (e.g. water).

Not all the molecules have exactly the same energy at a particular temperature. Some molecules in a liquid have more than average energy and if they are near the liquid surface they are able to escape; this is evaporation. If heat energy is supplied to the liquid the average energy of each molecule increases; that is they move faster. Eventually all the molecules have sufficient energy to break away from each other and so a gas is formed, in which all molecules move independently. This change of state is known as boiling.

The molecules of a gas move continually, colliding with each other and with the walls of their containing vessel. The laws of mechanics apply to these collisions; further they are elastic, that is, no knetic energy is lost. When a molecule bounces back from the walls of the container its momentum is changed and so it must have experienced a force. The force the molecules exert on the walls accounts for the pressure. If a gas is heated its molecules move faster and exert a greater pressure on the walls. An example of this effect is that if the pressure of a car or bicyle tyre is measured on a hot day it will be found to be greater than on a cold day, even though no gas has been allowed to enter or leave the tyre in the meantime.

In a gas the forces between the molecules are so small that the molecules can be considered to move independently of each other. A gas therefore fills all the available space and has no fixed volume or shape; it takes the volume and shape of the vessel containing it. When the pressure exerted by a gas is equal to atmospheric pressure its volume will be about 1000 times greater than the liquid from which it forms, and its density will therefore be about 1000 times less. This can be shown using the syringes illustrated in Fig. 8.1.

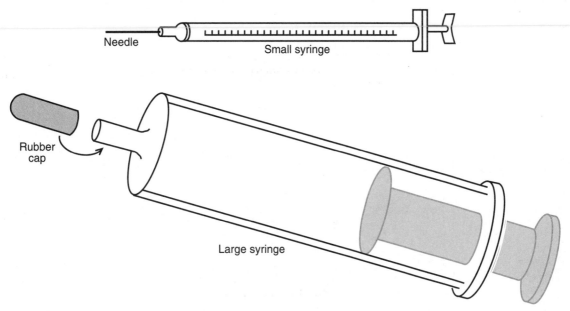

Fig. 8.1

A rubber cap is fitted over the end of the large syringe with its piston pushed down to zero volume. The small syringe with a hypodermic needle at its end is partially filled with water. 0.1 ml of water is then injected into the large syringe through the rubber cap via the hypodermic needle. When the needle is removed the cap seals. The large syringe is now inverted in a beaker of brine and the brine brought to the boil. The water in the syringe turns to steam and is seen to occupy a volume of about 100 ml; that is 1000 times larger than when it was water.

Evaporation takes place from the surface of a liquid at all temperatures, whereas boiling only occurs above a certain temperature and takes place throughout the liquid. However, the nearer the liquid is to its boiling temperature the faster the rate of evaporation.

Evaporation means that the faster molecules which happen to be near the surface escape from it. If the molecules which escape are free to move away from the space immediately above the liquid (or even encouraged to do so by a stream of air) evaporation will continue until the liquid has all evaporated. This is how puddles of water left on the road after rain eventually dry up. The higher the temperature of the liquid the quicker evaporation occurs.

As evaporation means that some of the more energetic molecules of the liquid are leaving it, the average energy of the molecules left behind falls; thus the liquid falls in temperature. For example, a bottle of milk may be kept cool by wrapping the bottle in a wet cloth. Some water evaporates from the cloth and the remaining water falls in temperature. In turn it extracts heat from the milk. This is more effective if the rate of evaporation can be speeded up by standing the wet bottle in a draught.

It is unwise for a human being to stand in a draught or breeze after taking violent exercise, however warm he feels. The perspiration on his body evaporates quickly under these conditions, thus cooling his body, and making it susceptible to a chill.

8.3 Brownian motion

The continual motion of molecules within a liquid or gas is call **Brownian motion**, after Robert Brown. In 1827 he used a microscope to examine pollen particles sprinkled on the surface of water and was surprised to notice that they were in a continuous state of haphazard movement. It appears that the motion of these relatively large particles is caused by the impact of moving water molecules. The same kind of movement can be seen in the case of smoke particles in air. The apparatus for this experiment is shown in Fig. 8.2.

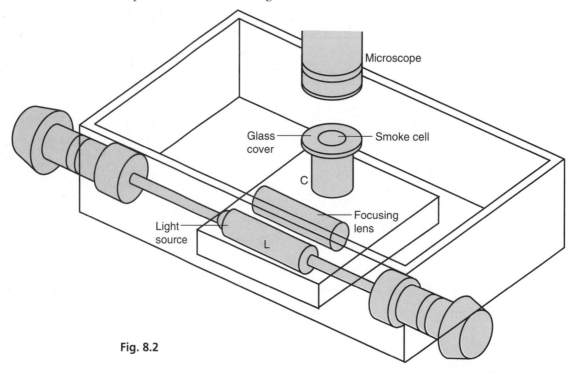

Fig. 8.2

It consists of a small transparent cell *C*, with a cover, strongly illuminated from the side by a light *L*. A piece of cord or rag is set smouldering and some of the smoke which contains minute particles is collected by a syringe and injected into the cell. The cover is replaced and the microscope focused on the cell. The particles are seen to be moving in an irregular way, darting about suddenly, and always in motion.

The irregular motion of a particle is due to the movement of air molecules, which bombard it from all sides. The particle is relatively small and so the number of air molecules hitting it on one side is not balanced by an equal number hitting the opposite side at the same instant. The smoke particle thus moves in the direction of the resultant force. The irregular motion of the particles shows that air molecules move rapidly in all directions. At higher temperatures the molecules move even more rapidly and the motion of the particles is even more violent and irregular.

If the particles in a gas are very much bigger than the molecules of the gas they do not show this irregular movement. This is because the large number of molecules hitting one side is not relatively much greater than the number hitting the other at the same moment. The resultant force is thus relatively very small and the large particle is not so easily moved. For example, a table tennis ball suspended in air does not move for this reason.

8.4 Diffusion

Diffusion provides further evidence for the irregular random motion of molecules. Consider the apparatus shown in Fig. 8.3.

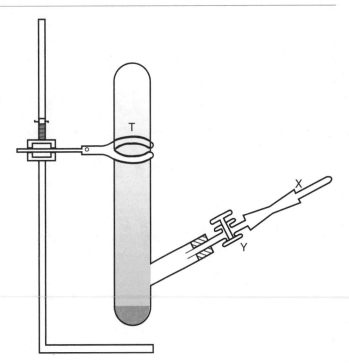

Fig. 8.3

The vertical tube T initially contains air. A capsule containing liquid bromine is placed in the end tube X and this is connected to the tap Y by means of a short length of thick-walled rubber tubing. The tap is closed and the capsule tapped until it moves down inside the rubber tubing. The tubing is then squeezed with a pair of pliers until the capsule breaks. Liquid bromine runs down to the tap which is then opened allowing the bromine to enter the tube T. If the tube is observed some minutes later the characteristic brown colour of the bromine will be seen to have diffused part way up the tube. This is made more obvious by placing a white card behind the tube. If the experiment is now repeated, with the tube T initially evacuated of air, the brown bromine vapour will fill the entire tube the moment the tap is opened.

The behaviour of the bromine in this experiment can only be explained by saying that the molecules of the bromine gas continually collide with air molecules in the first case. Their progress up the tube is thus impeded, whereas in the second case there are no air molecules to get in their way.

Summary

1   Any material can exist in one of three states, as a solid, a liquid or a gas.
2   Energy is required to change a solid to a liquid and a liquid to a gas. *While* the change of state is taking place there is *no change in temperature.*
3   The volume of any material is about the same when it is a liquid as when it is a solid.
4   When a material changes to a gas its volume increases about one thousand-fold.
5   The continual random motion of molecules within a liquid or gas is called **Brownian motion**.
6   Diffusion is the slow mixing of the molecules of one liquid or gas with another by the random motion of their molecules.

Chapter 9

Expansion of solids and liquids

9.1 Solids

As temperature increases, the molecules of a solid vibrate with greater amplitude, thus causing the total volume of the solid to increase; that is, a solid expands when heated. This expansion can be troublesome and very large forces may be set up if there is an obstruction to the free movement of the expanding body. Continuous welded rails used on most of our railway lines are held in place by strong concrete clamps and sleepers. They are stress-free at 25 °C but experience very large forces at high and low temperatures.

Modern motorways are often constructed with a concrete surface for economy. If this surface were laid in one continuous section, cracks would appear owing to the expansion and contraction brought about by the differing summer and winter temperatures. To avoid this, the surface is laid in short sections, each section being separated from the next by a small gap filled with black pitch. On a hot day the pitch is squeezed out by the expansion of the concrete. Allowance has to be made for the expansion of bridges and the roofs of buildings made of steel girders. A common way of overcoming these difficulties is to fix one end of the structure while the other rests on steel rollers.

Although expansion can be troublesome it can be useful. Steel plates such as those used in ship building are often rivetted together using red hot rivets. Holes are made in the overlapping plates, a red hot rivet pushed through and its head pressed tightly against one plate. The other end of the rivet is hammered until it is tight against the second plate. As the rivet cools it contracts thus pulling the two plates together. A watertight join is formed.

When strips of the same length but of different substances are heated through the same range of temperature, their expansions are not always equal. This difference may be used to make a thermostat. Figure 9.1 shows the principle of a thermostat which is a device for maintaining a steady temperature. The heater circuit is completed through the two contacts at C. One of the contacts is attached to the end of a metal strip S, the other to the end of a bimetallic strip M. On heating the brass expands more than the invar and the strip bends with the brass on the outside.

At a certain temperature the strip bends so much that the contacts are pulled apart thus breaking the circuit to the heater. When the air cools the bimetallic strip straightens, the contacts close and the heater switches on again. The thermostat may be set to operate at different temperatures by adjusting the knob K.

If the knob pushes the metal strip *S* towards the bimetallic strip a higher temperature is maintained.
Thermostats working on the same principle are used to control the temperature of electric irons, immersion heaters, aquaria for fish and for other purposes.

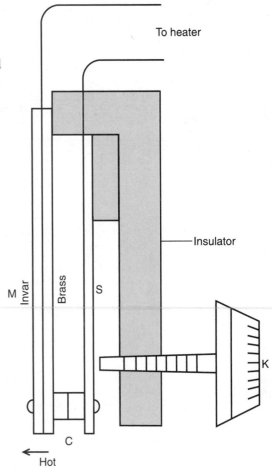

Fig. 9.1

9.2 Liquids

Liquids expand more than solids on heating. This may be shown by means of a flask fitted with a rubber bung and a length of glass tubing as shown in Fig. 9.2.
The flask is filled with a liquid and the bung pushed in until the level of liquid comes a short distance up the tube.
When the flask is plunged into hot water the liquid level is first seen to fall and then to rise.
The initial fall is due to the expansion of the glass which becomes heated first and expands before the heat has had time to reach the liquid.
Due to the expansion of the glass, the expansion of the liquid measured is less than its true expansion.
When the heat does reach the liquid, it causes the liquid level to rise above its initial level, showing that liquids expand more than solids on heating.

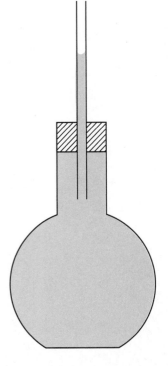

Fig. 9.2

If we take some water at 0 °C and begin to heat it the water contracts instead of expanding over the temperature range 0–4 °C. Its behaviour is unusual. At about 4 °C the water reaches its smallest volume, and thus its greatest density. Above 4 °C water expands in the normal way. The unusual behaviour of water means that between 0 °C and 4 °C water is less dense the colder it is. The colder water rises to the surface of a pond and it is here that ice first forms. A sheet of surface ice acts as a heat insulator and it takes a long time for the water below to freeze, thus thickening the ice. It is most unlikely that a pond of reasonable depth will freeze right through; thus pond life is able to survive below the ice.

9.3 Thermometers

We must be careful to distinguish the temperature of a body from the internal energy it contains (i.e. its heat energy). Temperature is a measure of the degree of hotness of a body whereas the energy it contains depends on its nature and mass as well as its temperature.

The temperature of a substance is a number which expresses its degree of hotness on some chosen scale. It is measured by means of a thermometer. Some thermometers depend on the expansion of a liquid when heated, some on the expansion of a bimetallic strip, and others on the change of other physical quantities brought about by heating; for example electrical resistance.

The most common thermometer in use is that which relies on the expansion of mercury in a glass tube when the mercury is heated. The mercury is contained in a bulb at the lower end of the tube. Above the mercury is some nitrogen. The glass tube is calibrated by dividing it into 100 equal divisions between two fixed points. The upper fixed point is marked on the tube when the thermometer is surrounded by steam boiling under standard atmospheric pressure. The lower fixed point is marked when the thermometer is in pure melting ice. The upper and lower fixed points are given the numbers 100 and zero, respectively. This procedure establishes the Centigrade or Celsius scale of temperature.

Mercury freezes at −39 °C and therefore a mercury in glass thermometer is not suitable for use in countries such as Russia and Canada which have very cold winters. In such places alcohol in glass thermometers are used, as alcohol remains liquid down to −115 °C. However, alcohol boils at a little above 70 °C and so is not suitable for high temperatures.

A clinical thermometer is one specially designed to measure the temperature of the human body. It is only necessary for it to have a range of a few degrees on either side of normal body temperature (37 °C). The thermometer is generally placed beneath the patient's tongue and left there for two minutes to ensure it acquires the body temperature. The stem has a narrow constriction in its bore just above the bulb (Fig. 9.3). Thus when the thermometer is removed from the mouth, the mercury beyond the constriction stays put while that below it contracts into the bulb. When the temperature reading has been taken, the mercury in the tube is returned to the bulb by shaking.

Constriction

Fig. 9.3

35   40   45

Summary

1   Solids and liquids both expand on heating (water only above 4 °C).
2   A thermostat relies on the different amounts of expansion of the two metals in the bimetallic strip for its operation.
3   Thermometers make use of the expansion of mercury or alcohol which occurs on heating.

Chapter 10
The behaviour of gases

The volume of a gas can be changed not only by altering its temperature, but also by changing the pressure exerted on it. Thus a gas has three quantities: **volume**, **temperature** and **pressure** all of which may change. In order to make a full study of the behaviour of a fixed mass of gas three separate experiments are therefore carried out to investigate:

1 the relation between volume and pressure at constant temperature (**Boyle's law**);

2 the relation between volume and temperature at constant pressure (**Charles' law**);

3 the relation between pressure and temperature at constant volume (**pressure law**).

10.1 Boyle's law

The volume of a fixed mass of gas is inversely proportional to the pressure, provided the temperature remains constant; that is, the pressure multiplied by the volume is constant.

$$pV = \text{constant}$$

One version of the apparatus used to show this law is illustrated in Fig. 10.1. It consists of a column of air trapped in a vertical tube by some oil with a low vapour pressure. Pressure is applied to the oil in the reservoir by a pump. The Bourdon gauge measures the pressure of the air above the oil in the reservoir. This is a little greater than the pressure of the air trapped in the tube, due to the vertical oil column, but the error is so small that for practical purposes it may be ignored.

Air is first pumped into the reservoir until the Bourdon gauge reaches its maximum reading. The tap is closed and readings taken of the length h of the trapped air column and also the pressure reading of the Bourdon gauge p. The tap is then opened to allow a little air to escape, closed again, and a further set of readings recorded. This procedure is repeated until the Bourdon gauge registers atmospheric pressure once more. It is possible, using a suction pump, to obtain readings below atmospheric pressure. If h is now plotted against $1/p$ a graph is obtained similar to that in Fig. 10.2.

As the volume V is proportional to the length of the column of trapped air h, the fact that the graph is a straight line through the origin shows that:

$$V \div 1/p = \text{a constant}$$

$$\text{or} \qquad pV = \text{a constant}$$

$$\text{or} \qquad p_1 V_1 = p_2 V_2 \text{ etc.} \qquad (10.1)$$

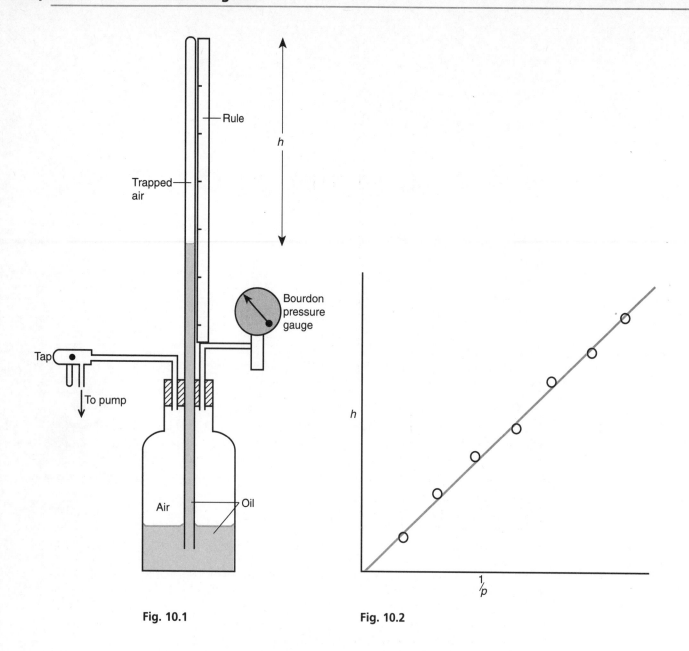

Fig. 10.1   Fig. 10.2

10.2 Charles' law

The volume of a fixed mass of gas is directly proportional to its absolute temperature provided the pressure remains constant; that is, the volume divided by the absolute temperature is constant.

$$\frac{V}{T} = \text{constant}$$

A simple apparatus for verifying this law is shown in Fig. 10.3. It consists of a capillary tube sealed at its lower end. Some air has been trapped in the tube by a short thread of mercury M. A centimetre scale is attached to the tube so that the length of the trapped air column can be easily noted. The capillary tube and scale are placed in a beaker of water alongside a thermometer T.

The temperature of the water and the length of the air column are first noted. The water is then heated through about 10 °C, time is allowed for the heat to reach the air, and the temperature and length of the air column are recorded. This process is repeated several times. The volume V of trapped air is proportional to the length of the column as the tube is of uniform bore. The trapped air is kept at constant pressure by the mercury index moving up the tube as the temperature increases.

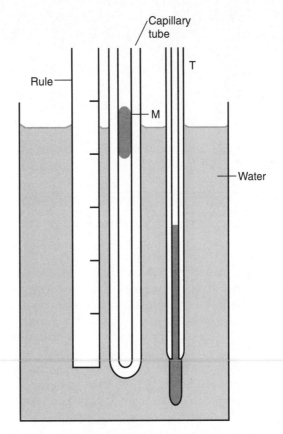

Fig. 10.3

From the results obtained a graph of length against temperature is plotted (Fig. 10.4). The graph is a straight line showing that air expands uniformly with temperature as measured on the mercury thermometer.

If the graph is produced backwards it cuts the temperature axis at a point which gives the temperature (−273 °C) at which the volume of the gas would contract to zero, assuming the gas continues to contract uniformly below 0 °C. As we cannot imagine it possible for a gas to have a volume of less than zero, it is reasonable to assume that −273 °C is the lowest temperature it is possible to obtain, and thus represents the absolute zero of temperature. This assumption cannot be directly tested by experiment as gases liquefy before they reach this temperature, and so the gas laws no longer apply. However, experiments have shown that while temperatures close to −273 °C have been reached, it has not been possible to go below this value.

The value −273 °C has thus been taken as the zero of a new scale of temperature called the **Absolute** or **Kelvin** scale. Temperatures on this scale are represented by T, and are expressed in units of K. Temperatures on the Celsius scale are converted to the Kelvin scale by adding 273. Thus 0 °C = 273 K.

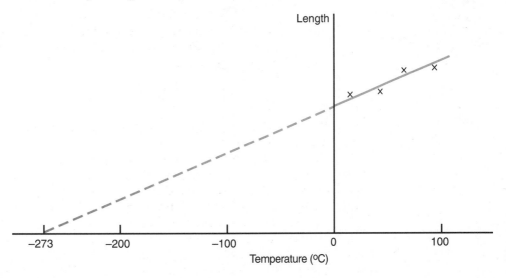

Fig. 10.4 Variation of volume with temperature at constant pressure

The graph in Fig. 10.4 is a straight line through the origin of our new temperature scale. Thus the volume of the gas is proportional to its temperature measured on the Kelvin scale and we may write:

$$V \propto T$$

or $\dfrac{V}{T}$ = a constant   (10.2)

or $\dfrac{V_1}{T_1} = \dfrac{V_2}{T_2}$ etc.

10.3 Pressure law

The pressure of a fixed mass of gas is directly proportional to its absolute temperature provided its volume remains constant; that is, the pressure divided by the absolute temperature is constant.

$$\frac{p}{T} = \textbf{constant}$$

The apparatus for demonstrating this law is shown in Fig. 10.5. It consists of a flask connected by rubber tubing to a Bourdon gauge. The flask is surrounded by water in a beaker. A thermometer T is also used.

The apparatus, particularly the rubber tubing, is first inspected for leaks. The temperature of the water and the reading on the Bourdon gauge are noted. The water is then heated while being stirred. After the temperature of the water has risen by about 10 °C, heating is stopped, time is allowed for the heat to reach the air in the flask, and then the temperature and the pressure are again noted. This procedure is repeated several times until the water is near boiling.

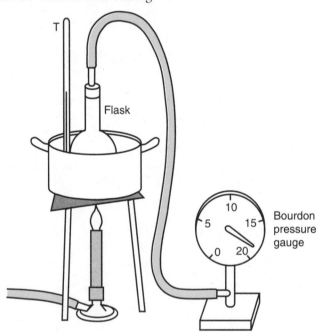

Fig. 10.5

From the results a graph of pressure against temperature is plotted (Fig. 10.6). It is a straight line passing through −273 °C or 0 K. Thus the pressure of the gas is proportional to its temperature measured on the Kelvin scale and we may write:

$$p \propto T$$

or $\dfrac{p}{T}$ = a constant   (10.3)

or $\dfrac{p_1}{T_1} = \dfrac{p_2}{T_2}$ etc.

This apparatus can be used to measure temperature (constant volume gas thermometer).

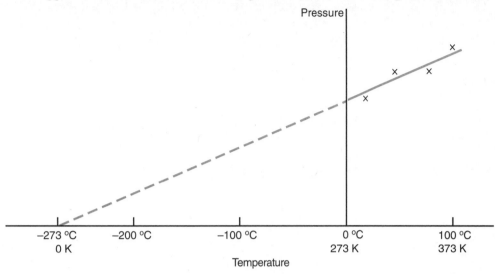

Fig. 10.6 Variation of pressure with temperature at constant volume

10.4 The universal gas law

The equations (10.1), (10.2) and (10.3) can be combined in a more general equation which we may write:

$$\frac{pV}{T} = \text{a constant} \tag{10.4}$$

or
$$\frac{p_1 V_1}{T_1} = \frac{p_2 V_2}{T_2} \text{ etc.} \tag{10.5}$$

If we always consider one mole (one gram molecular weight) of a gas, the constant is the same for all gases and we may write equation (10.4) as follows:

$$\frac{pV}{T} = R$$

where R is the universal gas constant.

Suppose a fixed mass of gas, occupying 1 litre at 27 °C, is heated to 227 °C and at the same time the pressure on the gas is doubled. We may find its final volume by using equation (10.5), but first we must convert the temperatures to the Kelvin scale.

$$27\,°C = 300\ K \quad \text{and} \quad 227\,°C = 500\ K \quad \text{and} \quad p_2 = 2p_1$$

$$\frac{p_1 V_1}{T_1} = \frac{p_2 V_2}{T_2}$$

thus
$$\frac{p_1 \times 1}{300} = \frac{2p_1 \times V_2}{500}$$

hence
$$V_2 = \frac{500}{300 \times 2} = \frac{5}{6}\ \text{litre}$$

10.5 Models of a gas

The following models give an idea of how we think molecules of a gas behave. The first model consists of several marbles placed on the base of a tray or baking tin. The tray is moved horizontally by hand in short, sharp random jerks. The marbles are seen to move, making random collisions with each other and the sides of the tray. To obtain a clear impression it is best to watch one marble carefully.

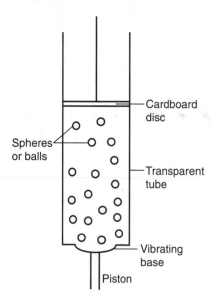

Fig. 10.7 Three-dimensional model of a gas

Although this model is useful, it is two-dimensional, whereas molecules move in three dimensions. Figure 10.7 shows a better model. Some small polystyrene spheres or phosphor bronze ball bearings are contained in a vertical transparent tube. The base of the tube is connected to a piston which is driven by an electric motor. The oscillating piston causes the base to vibrate; the frequency of vibration is changed by altering the speed of the motor. An alternative arrangement is to use a loudspeaker as the base of the tube and to connect the loudspeaker to a signal generator the frequency of which can be altered.

When the base vibrates, the spheres on it are thrown into random motion in the cylinder. They collide with each other and with the walls of the container on which they thus exert a pressure. They also exert a pressure on the cardboard disc which sits on top of them. If the amplitude of vibration of the base is increased, the average energy of the spheres is increased. The spheres thus move faster and keep the disc at a higher level. This illustrates the expansion of a gas when it is heated at constant pressure. Instead of allowing the disc to rise when the spheres are made to move faster, masses can be added to the top of the disc to keep it at the same height. The masses increase the external pressure that the disc exerts on the spheres. This illustrates the increase in the pressure that a gas exerts when it is heated at constant volume.

Summary

1   For a fixed mass of gas the following equation is true:

$$\frac{pV}{T} = \text{a constant}$$

where p is the pressure of the gas, V the volume that it occupies and T its temperature on the Kelvin scale (°C + 273).

2   If one mole of gas is used the equation becomes

$$\frac{pV}{T} = R$$

where R is the universal gas constant.

3   If one of the quantities p, V or T is kept constant three simpler equations may be used. They are

$$pV = \text{a constant, when } T \text{ is kept constant}$$

$$\frac{p}{T} = \text{a constant, when } V \text{ is kept constant}$$

$$\frac{V}{T} = \text{a constant, when } p \text{ is kept constant}$$

Chapter 11
Specific heat capacity

Heat is a form of energy and like any other form of energy it is measured in joules.

If we take equal masses of water and oil and warm them for the same time in separate containers using similar immersion heaters, the temperature of the water will rise much less than the temperature of the oil. We say these substances have different specific heat capacities.

The specific heat capacity of a substance is the quantity of heat required to raise the temperature of one kilogram of it by 1 K. It has units of joules per kilogram per kelvin (J/kg K).

It follows that if m kilograms of a substance, of specific heat capacity c, are to be raised in temperature by θ K, then the heat required will be $mc\theta$ joules.

$$\text{Heat required} = mc\theta \text{ joules}$$

It happens that for water 4200 joules of heat are required to raise the temperature of one kilogram by 1 K. The specific heat capacity of water is thus 4200 J/kg K. This value is high compared with most other substances. A great deal of energy is required to raise the temperature of water a certain amount compared with the same mass of another substance. Likewise water cools more slowly because it contains more energy than the same mass of other substances at the same temperature. Water is therefore used to fill radiators and hot water bottles.

11.1 To measure the specific heat capacity of a solid

The temperature of an object can be raised by supplying energy to it in various ways:

1. Mechanical energy can be supplied by allowing the object to fall through a height h, when the energy supplied is equal to mgh.

2. The energy can be obtained from another hot body of mass m, and specific heat capacity c. The energy supplied is equal to $mc\theta$, where θ is its temperature change.

3. The energy can be supplied by an electric current I, flowing for a time t, through a wire across which a potential difference of V is maintained (see Unit 20.7).

$$\text{Energy supplied} = VIt$$

The mechanical method may be used to determine the specific heat capacity of lead shot. The temperature of about 0.25 kg of lead shot is recorded. It is then placed in a wide tube about one metre long, and rubber bungs fitted at each end of the tube. The tube is smartly inverted about 100 times, the number n of inversions being counted. One bung is removed from the tube and the temperature of the lead shot again measured. The specific heat capacity c is calculated from the equation:

$$n \times mgh = mc\theta$$

If two substances at different temperatures are mixed and come to a common temperature, the heat lost by one in cooling will be equal to the heat gained by the other, providing no heat is gained from or lost to the surroundings.

The specific heat capacity of a solid can be found by warming it to a high temperature and then quickly transferring it to a calorimeter containing cold water. The water and calorimeter receive heat from the solid and all three finally reach the same temperature. The calorimeter should either be made from a material which is a very poor conductor, in which case it can be assumed to take no heat, or from a material such as copper which is such a good conductor that it can be assumed to have the same temperature as its contents.

Details of an experiment to find the specific heat capacity of copper using a copper calorimeter are as follows. A large piece of copper, with a thread attached to it, is placed in a beaker of boiling water and left for some time. While the copper is warming to 100 °C, a copper calorimeter is weighed empty and then about two-thirds full of cold water. The calorimeter is then placed inside a jacket and a thermometer placed in it.

When the piece of copper has been in the boiling water long enough to reach 100 °C, the temperature of the cold water is noted, and the copper transferred from the boiling to the cold water. The mixture is gently stirred by moving the piece of copper in the water by means of the thread. The final steady maximum temperature is noted. The piece of copper is then dried and weighed.

The heat lost by the solid is then equated to the heat gained by the calorimeter and the cold water. The specific heat capacity of copper is the only unknown in the equation and can be calculated.

Example

Suppose the following readings have been obtained:

mass of calorimeter empty	m_1 = 0.1 kg
mass of water in calorimeter	m_2 = 0.1 kg
mass of piece of copper	m_3 = 0.2 kg
temperature of cold water	θ_1 = 10 °C
temperature of boiling water	θ_2 = 100 °C
temperature of mixture	θ_3 = 20 °C
specific heat capacity of water	c_1 = 4200 J/kg K

Heat gained by calorimeter and water = heat lost by piece of copper. Thus

$$m_1 c(\theta_3 - \theta_1) + m_2 c_1 (\theta_3 - \theta_1) = m_3 c(\theta_2 - \theta_3)$$

hence $\quad$ $0.1c \times 10 + 0.1 \times 4200 \times 10 = 0.2c \times 80$

and $\qquad\qquad\qquad\qquad\qquad 15c = 4200$

$$c = 280 \text{ J/kg K}$$

Although the method just described is a reasonable one, it is open to two serious errors: some hot water is carried across to the calorimeter on the hot solid and the hot solid loses heat during the transfer. Both errors can be reduced with care but not eliminated.

A better method is one based on the steady heating of a block of the solid by a heater immersed in it, as shown in Fig. 11.1.

A 12 V immersion heater *H*, with a power of 24 or 36 W, is sunk into a hole specially drilled in the solid for this purpose. It is convenient, but not essential, if the block has a mass of 1 kg. A second, smaller hole in the block contains a thermometer *T*. To ensure good thermal contact between the heater and block and the thermometer and block, a few drops of thin oil are placed in each hole. The block can be surrounded by an insulating jacket to reduce heat losses.

The apparatus is connected up and switched on for a known time (between 10 and 30 minutes depending on the material of the block). During this time the voltage and current are kept as constant as possible, by adjusting the variable resistor *R*, and their values noted. At the beginning and end of the experiment the temperature of the block is noted. The specific heat capacity *c* of the material of the block is worked out using the equation:

energy supplied electrically = heat gained by the block,

$$VIt = mc(\theta_2 - \theta_1)$$

where θ_1 and θ_2 are the initial and final temperatures of the block.

As well as avoiding the errors present in the method of mixtures, this method requires no calorimeter.

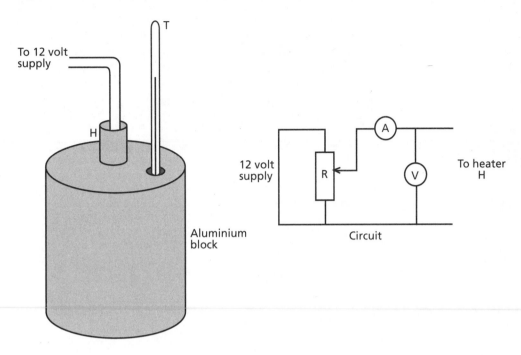

Fig. 11.1

11.2 To measure the specific heat capacity of a liquid

If the specific heat capacity of a solid is known, the method of mixtures may be used to find the specific heat capacity of a liquid. The calorimeter is two-thirds filled with the liquid under test instead of water. The procedure and calculations are then the same as already described for finding the specific heat capacity of a solid.

However, the electrical heating method just described for a solid is again superior. The liquid (1 kg for convenience) is contained in an aluminium saucepan. The heater is immersed in the liquid, care being taken not to short the connections. The procedure is the same as that described for a solid. Strictly speaking, in working out the specific heat capacity of the liquid, account should be taken of the heat used in raising the temperature of the aluminium saucepan. However, both the mass and specific heat capacity of aluminium are likely to be much less than the values for the liquid, so no great error is involved in ignoring the heat taken in by the saucepan. Calculation of the result is then the same as for a solid.

Summary

1 The specific heat capacity of a substance is the quantity of heat required to raise the temperature of one kilogram of it by 1 K. It has units of joules per kilogram per kelvin (J/kg K).

2 The heat required to change the mass m of a substance by a temperature of θ kelvin is given by

$$\text{heat required} = mc\theta \text{ joules}$$

where c is the specific heat capacity of the substance.

3 The specific heat capacity of a solid or liquid is usually measured electrically, the electrical energy supplied being equal to VIt joules.

Chapter 12
Heat transfer

Heat is transferred from one place to another in one of three ways: **conduction**, **radiation** or **convection**.

12.1 Conduction

If a metal spoon is left in a teacup for a short length of time the handle becomes warm. Heat travels along the spoon by means of conduction. Metals contain electrons which are very loosely attached to atoms, and are easily removed from them. When a metal is heated these 'free electrons' gain kinetic energy and move independently of the atoms. They drift towards the cooler parts of the metal thus spreading the energy to those regions.

In substances where no free electrons are present the energy is conveyed from one atom to another by collision. This is a much slower process and such substances are called poor conductors of heat.

Most metals are good conductors of both heat and electricity, free electrons being responsible for both. Substances such as wool, cotton, cork and wood are bad conductors. A number of materials lie between these extremes. The best saucepans are made of copper as heat is rapidly conducted through this metal. Many materials are poor conductors of heat because they trap tiny pockets of air between their fibres, and air, like all gases, is a poor conductor of heat. Textiles and glass fibre are examples. Glass fibre is frequently used as lagging for attics and hot water tanks.

12.2 Comparison of thermal conductivities

Similar rods, made of different materials, pass through corks inserted in holes made in the side of a metal tank (Fig. 12.1). The rods are first coated in wax by dipping them into molten wax and then allowing it to cool. Boiling water is then poured into the tank, so that the ends of the rods are all heated to the same temperature. After some time it is seen that the wax has melted to different distances along the rods, showing differences in their **thermal conductivities**.

In the kitchen, saucepans are made of metals such as copper or aluminium, which are good heat conductors. However, the handles of saucepans are made of insulators, such as plastic or wood, so that the utensils can be handled when hot. The handles of kettles and oven doors must be made of similar materials.

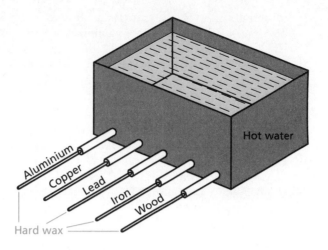

Fig. 12.1 Conduction

12.3 Radiation

Both conduction and convection are ways of conveying heat from one place to another which require the presence of a material. Radiation does not require a material medium; it is the means by which heat travels from the Sun through the empty space beyond the Earth's atmosphere. Radiation consists of electromagnetic waves which pass through a vacuum. On striking a body these waves are partly reflected and partly absorbed, and can cause a rise in temperature.

The rate at which a body radiates depends on its temperature and the nature of its surface. For a given temperature, a body radiates most energy when its surface is dull black and least when its surface is highly polished. A comparison of the radiating powers of different surfaces may be made using a Leslie cube. This is a hollow metal cube, each side of which has a different surface; one is dull black, one highly polished, another may be shiny black and the fourth painted white. The cube is filled with hot water and a thermometer with a blackened bulb placed at the same distance from each face in turn (Fig. 12.2). In each case the thermometer reading is noted.

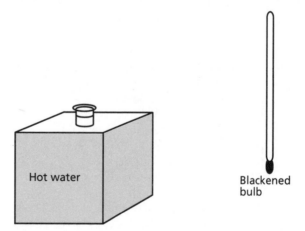

Fig. 12.2 Radiation
– Leslie's cube

The results show that the dull black surface produces the highest reading and the highly polished one the lowest. This indicates that the dull black surface is the best radiator and the highly polished one the worst.

The absorbing powers of different surfaces may be compared using a small electric fire (Fig. 12.3). The fire is placed about 10 to 15 cm behind a heat insulating screen, faced with a polished metal surface towards the fire. The screen has a hole in it 2 or 3 cm in diameter. If a piece of aluminium foil is attached to the back of one's hand by damping it, it is found that the hand may be held over the hole in the screen without discomfort. If the foil is now painted over with lamp black (or matt black paint) and the hand again placed over the hole, the hand has to be removed after a few seconds or it becomes burnt. This shows that a dull black surface is a good absorber of heat as well as a good radiator, whereas a highly polished surface is poor in both respects.

Radiation from the Sun is mostly in the form of visible light and infrared rays. These pass through glass and hence may reach the ground and plants inside a greenhouse, which absorb them. These objects also radiate, but due to their relatively low temperature, the infrared rays they emit are of longer wavelength and cannot penetrate the glass. The energy is thus trapped inside the greenhouse.

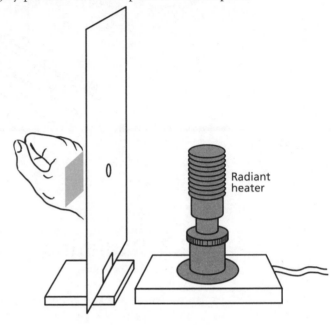

Fig. 12.3 Radiation

12.4 Convection

When a vessel containing a liquid is heated at the bottom, the liquid in that region becomes warm, less dense, and as a result rises. Its place is taken by cooler, more dense liquid moving downwards. In **convection** the heat is carried from one place to another by the movement of the molecules of the liquid. The existence of convection currents may be shown by dropping a large crystal of potassium permanganate to the bottom of a beaker of water. The beaker is gently heated under the crystal, which should be near the centre of the base. An upward current of coloured water will rise from the place where the heat is applied. This current spreads out at the surface and then moves down the sides of the beaker (Fig. 12.4). A domestic hot water system relies on convection currents for its functioning.

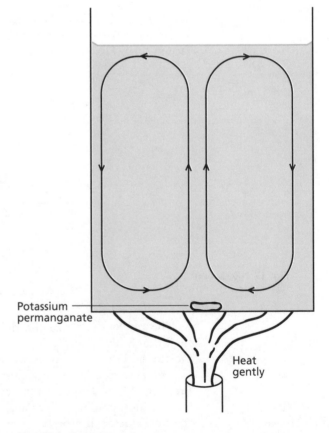

Fig. 12.4 Convection

Convection currents exist in gases as well as liquids. Warm air, for example, is less dense than cold air and rises. Cooler air then moves in to replace it. It is this process which is responsible for sea breezes towards the end of a warm summer's day. The relatively dark land absorbs more heat than the sea. Its specific heat capacity is less than that of water. As a result of both of these facts it reaches a higher temperature than the sea towards the end of a summer's day. The land warms the air over it which rises and is replaced by the cooler air from over the sea. Late on a clear summer's night the reverse is likely.

12.5 Preventing heat transfer

Fat and air are good insulators. Seals have a thick layer of fat surrounding their body and can survive all winter in very cold Arctic waters where we would perish in a few minutes. Birds have feathers; other animals have thick fur. Both reduce heat transfer by trapping a layer of air next to the body, that is they prevent convection currents in the air next to the body. In cold weather we wear layers of clothing made from materials such as wool. These materials trap air in a similar way to birds' feathers.

A home may have draught excluders, loft insulation, cavity-wall insulation, double glazing or several of these. Draught excluders stuck around doors and windows prevent the loss of warm air to the outside. Loft insulation consists of mineral wool or vermiculite which traps the air between the joists, thus preventing loss of heat due to convection currents. In a similar way cavity-wall insulation (often foam) prevents air circulating between the two layers of bricks. In double glazing the layer of air between the two glass sheets acts as an insulator. The layer must be thin to prevent convection currents.

Summary

1   Heat is transferred from one place to another by conduction, convection or radiation.

2   Conduction takes place in solids. In good conductors such as metals 'free electrons' gain kinetic energy and move independently of the atoms. They move to the cooler parts of the solid thus spreading the energy to those regions. In substances where no 'free electrons' are present the energy moves from one atom to another by collision. This is a much slower process and such substances are called poor conductors of heat.

3   Radiation takes place by the transmission of electromagnetic waves from a hot body to any other object. Radiation can take place through a vacuum as in the case of heat from the Sun reaching the Earth.

4   When liquids or gases are heated their density decreases and the warm liquid or gas rises. Cooler liquid or gas falls to take its place. Convection currents are set up and heat is transmitted from one place to another.

Chapter 13
Introduction to waves

13.1 Progressive waves

The idea of **progressive waves** is best illustrated using a spiral spring or 'slinky' stretched on a bench (Fig. 13.1). If one end of the spring is shaken at right angles to its length (Fig. 13.1(a)) a wave is seen to travel along the spring. As the wave is moving it is said to be progressive. In this example the motion causing the wave is at right angles to the direction of travel of the wave and the wave is termed **transverse**. In Fig. 13.1(b) one end of the spring is shaken in the direction of the spring's length and a concertina effect travels the length of the spring. In this case the motion causing the wave is in the same direction as the wave travels and the wave is called **longitudinal**.

(a)   Vibration

Vibration
(b)

Fig. 13.1 Waves along a spring: (a) transverse; (b) longitudinal

Examples of transverse waves are television, radio, heat, light, ultraviolet, X-rays, γ-rays (all electromagnetic waves) and water waves. In electromagnetic waves the electric and magnetic disturbances are at right angles to the direction the wave travels. At any moment a transverse wave has the shape of a sine wave and can be drawn as such (Fig. 13.2).

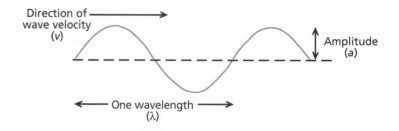

Direction of wave velocity (*v*)

Amplitude (*a*)

One wavelength (λ)

Fig. 13.2 Sine curve representing wave motion

Sound, on the other hand, is a longitudinal wave motion. The molecules of the material through which the sound travels vibrate to and fro along the direction of motion of the wave. At a given time each molecule is at a different point in its motion. A longitudinal wave may be represented by a sine curve, but it must be remembered that although the y direction still represents the size of the displacement, the direction of the displacement is in fact parallel to the direction of travel of the wave.

In Fig. 13.2 the **amplitude of the wave** is denoted by a. The amplitude represents the maximum displacement of the wave from the zero position. The distance between corresponding points on two successive waves is known as the **wavelength** λ. The number of waves produced every second by the source is called the **frequency f**. The length of wave motion produced every second by the source is the number of waves produced per second (f) multiplied by the length of each wave (λ). This product is clearly the speed v of the wave motion. Thus

$$v = f\lambda$$

It is usual to measure the speed in metres per second, the frequency in hertz and the wavelength in metres.

13.2 The ripple tank

A good understanding of the properties of all types of waves can be obtained from studying the behaviour of water waves in a ripple tank. The construction of a ripple tank is shown in Fig. 13.3.

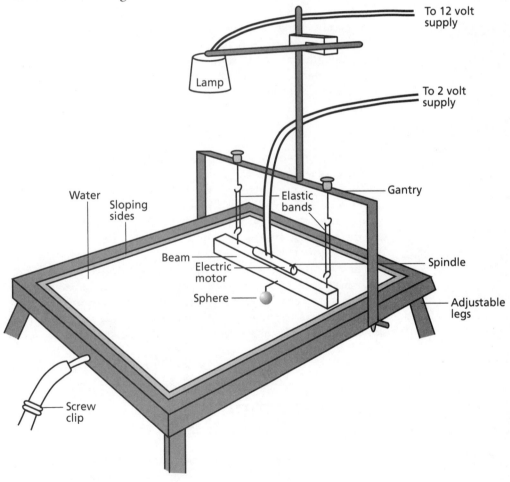

Fig. 13.3 A ripple tank

The apparatus consists of a shallow tray with a glass bottom and sloping sides to reduce reflection. The tray is mounted on four legs, each of which can be adjusted in length by a screw foot. In this way the tray can be levelled. A gantry stands above one end of the tank. On this gantry is a post on which a lamp is fixed. A beam, with a motor mounted on its top, is suspended from the gantry. A number of spheres, each of which may be lowered to project below the beam, are fixed to it.

The behaviour of the waves is best seen by using the lamp to cast a shadow of the water surface on a sheet of paper below the tank. Wave peaks and troughs are clearly seen on the paper. In diagrams lines are drawn to represent the peaks or troughs. These lines may be considered to represent the surface over which energy from the source spreads out, and are called **wavefronts**.

Two simple types of wave formation are worth studying; straight and circular waves. A small number of straight waves may conveniently be made by rolling a short length of dowel rod to and fro on the bottom of the tank. A few circular waves may be produced by touching the water surface with a pencil the required number of times.

For many experiments it is necessary to produce a continuous series of waves of one or other type.
This is done by connecting the motor to a suitable power unit (often 2 V d.c.) whereupon the spindle which is unevenly weighted, sets the beam bouncing up and down.

The speed of the motor determines the frequency of the waves.
If straight waves are required the lower edge of the beam should be a few millimetres below the water surface; if circular waves are wanted then the beam should be raised clear of the surface but one or more spheres turned down so that they are partly submerged by the same amount.

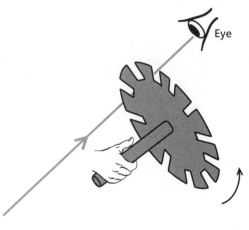

Fig. 13.4 Hand stroboscope

When the motor is producing a continuous series of waves it is often very difficult, if not impossible, for the eye to follow them across the paper below the tank. If this is so, it is helpful to use a hand stroboscope to 'freeze' the picture of the waves. A typical stroboscope is shown in Fig. 13.4. The handle is held in one hand while the disc is rotated using one finger of the other hand. The rotating disc is placed between the face and the wave pattern on the paper. The speed of rotation of the disc is increased until the waves appear stationary.

The slits in the disc allow glimpses of the waves at equal intervals of time. At one particular speed of rotation each wave moves forward to the position of the wave in front of it, in between successive glimpses. The wave pattern thus appears stationary. If the stroboscope is rotated slightly more slowly the wave pattern appears to be moving slowly forward. The opposite is the case if the disc is rotated slightly too fast.

13.3 Reflection

To see reflection clearly only a small number of waves are required. Therefore it is best if the ripple tank motor is not used, the waves being produced in the way already described. Figure 13.5 shows the results of the incidence of both straight and circular waves on straight and circular reflecting barriers R.

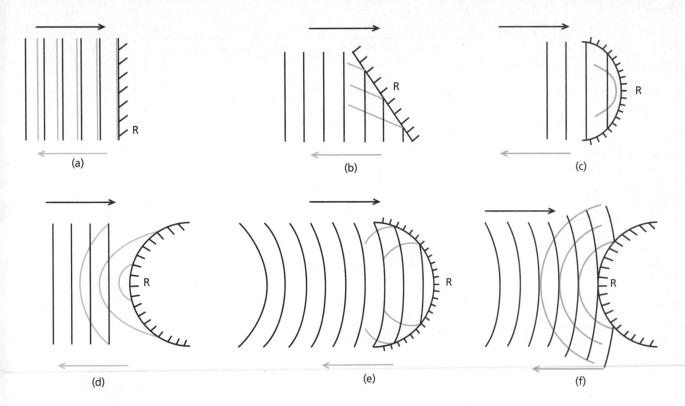

Fig. 13.5 Reflection of waves

In each case the behaviour of the waves after reflection can be worked out by considering which part of the incoming waves reaches the particular barrier first. This part of the wave will be reflected first. For example, in Fig. 13.5(d), the centre of each incoming straight wave obviously strikes the reflecting barrier first. The centre of each returning wave will therefore be in front, giving the curved shape shown.

In Fig. 13.5(c) and (e) the waves after reflection are approximately circular and converge to a point. This point is the image formed by waves from the point source (a distant source in Fig. 13.5(c)) after reflection at the barrier. In Fig. 13.5(d) the reflected waves appear to come from a point behind the barrier. This point represents a virtual image of the source.

13.4 Refraction

If water waves come to a region where their speed changes abruptly, then their direction of travel may change abruptly. This is called refraction. The best way of achieving this change in speed is to alter the depth of water by placing a sheet of glass in the tray of the ripple tank, since it is found that if the water is shallower the speed is reduced. This can be seen as waves approach a sloping beach. The body of the waves slows, but the crest is less affected and falls forward, causing the waves to break.

The sheet of glass should be placed in the tray so that it is covered by water to a depth of only one or two millimetres. A little experimentation will give the best depth. Straight waves, produced by either the beam or dowel rod, reach the leading edge of the glass plate at an angle (Fig. 13.6). As soon as part of the wave comes over the shallow region it slows down. It is clear that the end of the wave which has been in the shallow region longer will fall behind the other end. Thus the direction of the wavefront changes as shown.

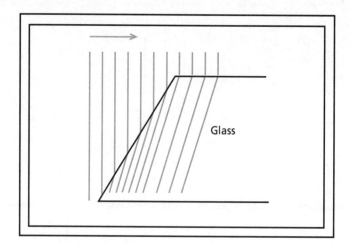

Fig. 13.6
Refraction of
waves at a plane
boundary

13.5 Interference

If water waves from two sources with the same frequency and similar amplitude meet, complete calm can be seen on some regions of the water surface. The waves are said to **interfere**.

Two spheres near the centre of the beam in the ripple tank are turned down so that when the beam vibrates two sets of circular waves are produced (Fig. 13.7). The interference pattern produced is shown in the same diagram.

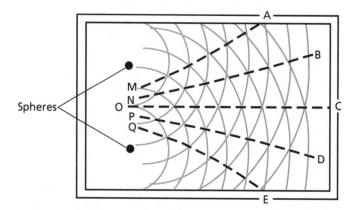

Fig. 13.7 Interference
of waves

The two spheres vibrate in step and thus points along the line *OC*, which are all equidistant from the two spheres, will always receive the waves in step. Along this line the waves will always **reinforce** each other making the actual displacement greater than either wave taken separately (Fig. 13.8(a)). In Fig. 13.7 points on the lines *NB* and *PD* are a distance of one wavelength further from one sphere than the other. Thus waves from the two spheres will arrive at each of these points one complete wavelength out of step and will again reinforce, as peaks arrive together. The same reasoning holds for lines *MA* and *QE*, except that the distance of each point from the two spheres differs by two wavelengths.

There will be directions between the lines mentioned along which points will be a distance of one, three, five, etc, half wavelengths further from one sphere than the other. Waves will arrive at these points either one, three or five (or any odd number) half wavelengths out of step. Thus complete **cancellation** of the two sets of waves will always occur at these points (Fig. 13.8(b)).

If the wavelength is reduced a smaller path difference is required for the waves from the two sources to be out of step by one, two, three, etc, complete wavelengths. Thus the lines in Fig. 13.7 come closer together and more regions of addition and cancellation of waves are seen in the tray. The reverse is true if the wavelength is increased.

If the two sources of waves are brought closer together the lines in Fig. 13.7 become further apart and fewer regions of addition and cancellation of waves are seen in the tray. If the sources are moved further apart the reverse is true.

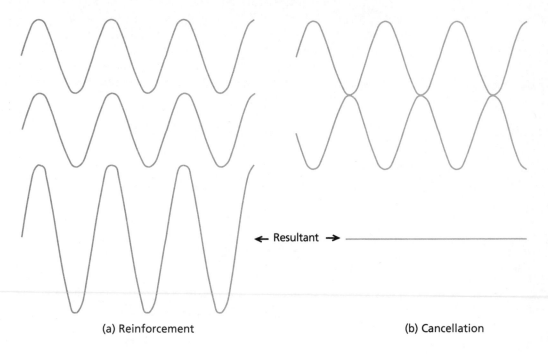

(a) Reinforcement   ← Resultant →   (b) Cancellation

Fig. 13.8 Addition of waves: (a) in step – reinforcement; (b) out of step – cancellation

13.6 Diffraction

If straight water waves are passed through a narrow gap in a barrier or past a small object some bending of the waves round the edges of the barrier or the object is noticed. Thus some change in the direction of travel of the waves occurs round these edges. This effect is called **diffraction**.

For diffraction to be obvious the size of the gap or object has to be about the same as the wavelength of the waves. In Fig. 13.9(a) the gap between the barriers is much greater than the wavelength and little bending occurs. In Fig. 13.9(b) the gap size and the wavelength are about the same and the bending is marked. In fact the waves become circular after passing through the gap and look the same as if the gap were replaced by a point source of waves. In Fig. 13.9(c) where the object is about the same width as the wavelength the bending is again very noticeable.

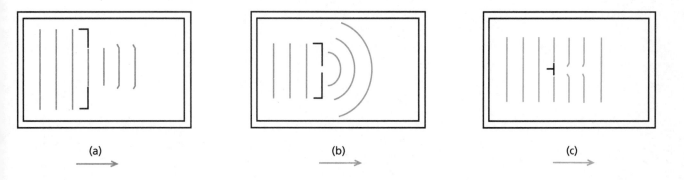

(a)   (b)   (c)

Fig. 13.9 Diffraction of waves: (a) wide gap; (b) narrow gap; (c) small object

The interference experiment described in the last unit may be carried out by allowing a series of straight waves to pass through two gaps in a barrier. After passing through the waves spread out in a semicircular fashion; that is they are diffracted, and produce the same interference pattern as was obtained with the two vibrating spheres. It should be noted that interference only occurs in this version of the experiment because diffraction take place at the narrow gaps. If diffraction did not take place the waves would never meet.

A clear understanding of the behaviour of water waves discussed in this chapter will make it easier to understand the properties of light and sound waves discussed in later chapters, as they behave in a similar way.

Summary

1   There are two types of waves:
    (a) Longitudinal waves in which the motion causing the wave is in the same direction as the wave travels.
    (b) Transverse waves in which the motion causing the wave is at right angles to the direction in which the wave travels.

2   All types of wave motion, other than sound, are transverse. Sound is a longitudinal wave motion.

3   The equation connecting the velocity v, the frequency f and the wavelength λ of a wave motion is

$$v = f\lambda$$

It is usual to measure the velocity in metres per second (m/s), the frequency in hertz (Hz) and the wavelength in metres (m).

4   Reflection is the change in direction of a wave when it hits a solid boundary.

5   Refraction is the change in direction of a wave motion caused by its change in speed.

6   Diffraction is the spreading out which occurs when waves pass round a small object or through a narrow gap.

7   Interference is the result of two wave motions meeting.

Chapter 14

The passage and reflection of light

In some light experiments it is more convenient to consider the behaviour of **rays** rather than wavefronts. Rays are lines drawn at right angles to wavefronts and thus represent the direction in which the wave is travelling. A ray box is a device for producing rays; one version is shown in Fig. 14.1.

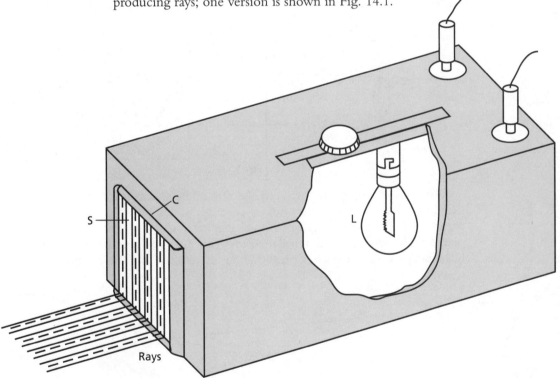

Fig. 14.1 Ray box

A small filament lamp L is enclosed in a box with a cylindrical convex lens C and a 'comb' S containing parallel slits in front of it. A diverging, converging or parallel beam of rays (Fig. 14.2) may be obtained by moving the lamp L.

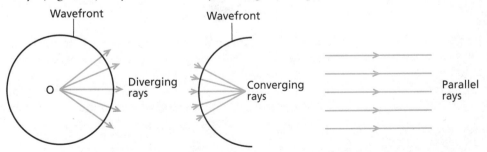

Fig. 14.2

14.1 Rectilinear propagation

If a ray box is placed on a sheet of white paper and switched on, a ray is obtained through each slit of the comb. This ray is actually a very narrow beam of light with straight sharp edges. It can be said that light travels in straight lines (**rectilinear propagation**) in this case. The existence of shadows and eclipses of the Sun and Moon is further evidence that light travels in straight lines.

When an obstacle is placed in the path of light coming from a point source the shadow formed on a screen is uniformly dark and has sharp edges (Fig. 14.3). As no light reaches the region of shadow (umbra) it is concluded that light travels in straight lines.

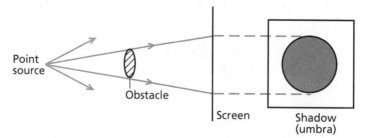

Fig. 14.3

If an extended light source is used the shadow is edged with a border of partial shadow (penumbra). The area of partial shadow receives light from some points on the source, but other points on the source are obscured from it by the obstacle (Fig. 14.4).

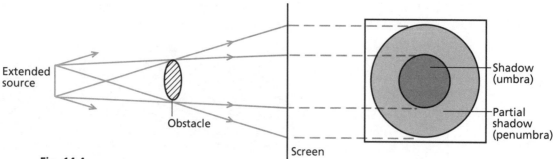

Fig. 14.4

When the Moon passes between the Sun and the Earth it casts a shadow or partial shadow on parts of the Earth's surface (Fig. 14.5). This effect is known as an eclipse or partial eclipse of the Sun. Area *c* is total shadow, *b* and *d* are partial shadow, and *a* and *e* receive light from the whole of the Sun's surface. On some occasions the Moon is a little further from the Earth than shown in the diagram and there is no area of complete shadow.

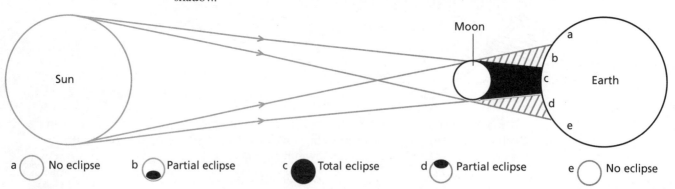

Fig. 14.5 Eclipse of the Sun

The pin–hole camera relies on the fact that light travels in straight lines to produce a clear image. It is a very simple version of a camera, invented well before lenses were used to produce images (Fig. 14.6(a)).

A pin–hole camera may be made by removing the back of a small cardboard or metal box, and replacing it with a piece of semi-transparent paper (the screen). A pin–hole is punched in the side of the box opposite the screen. When the hole is held towards a bright lamp, such as a carbon filament lamp, in a darkened room, an inverted image of the lamp filament can be seen on the screen. A narrow beam of light from point *A* on the source enters the camera through the pin-hole and strikes the screen at *A′*. Likewise light from *B* arrives at *B′*. Narrow beams of light from all the different points on the object will fall on the screen between *A′* and *B′*. Each point on the object is thus responsible for a point of light on the screen and a complete inverted image is seen. This image is formed on a screen and is said to be **real**. An image which cannot be shown on a screen, but only seen by the eye, is called **virtual**.

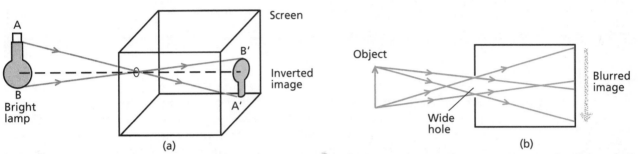

Fig. 14.6 Pin-hole camera

If the pin-hole camera is moved closer to the lamp the image becomes bigger. The small hole means that little light enters the camera. A larger hole would improve this, but would lead to blurring of the image (Fig. 14.6(b)), unless a lens was used. Thus the exposure time needed to produce a picture on a film using a pin-hole camera is long.

14.2 Reflection at a plane surface

Reflection of light may be examined by using a plane mirror supported vertically on a sheet of white paper. A line *XN*, the normal, is drawn at right angles to the mirror surface so that *N* is near the centre of the mirror (Fig. 14.7). Further lines are drawn from *N* so that they are inclined at angles such as 20°, 30°, etc., to *XN*. A ray box is now placed so that a single ray follows one of the drawn lines. The position of the reflected ray is marked with dots. The ray box is moved to each of the lines in turn and the procedure repeated. In each case the angle of incidence *i* of the ray is noted and the corresponding angle of reflection *r* measured. Within the limits of experimental accuracy the two are found to be equal.

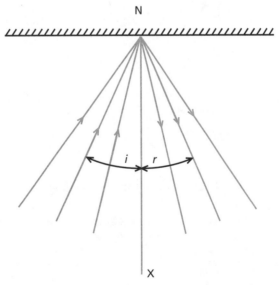

Fig. 14.7 Reflection at a plane mirror

The laws of reflection at plane surfaces are summarized as follows:

❶ **The incident ray, the reflected ray and the normal all lie in the same plane.**

❷ **The angle of incidence equals the angle of reflection.**

If a beam of divergent rays is reflected from a plane mirror, the rays will appear as in Fig. 14.8(a). A beam of convergent rays would give Fig. 14.8(b).

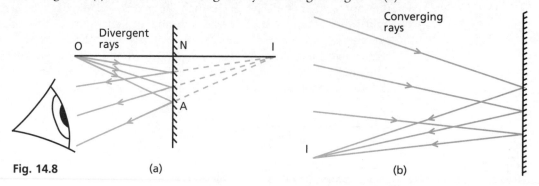

Fig. 14.8   (a)   (b)

In Fig. 14.8(a) the image I is the point from which rays entering the eye appear to have come. These rays have been reflected according to the laws just stated and consideration of the triangles ONA and INA will show that they are similar. Thus the distance IN is the same as the distance ON; that is the image is as far behind the surface of the mirror as the object is in front of it. As the rays do not actually come from I the image is virtual. In Fig. 14.8(b) the reflected rays cross at the point I to form a real image there.

If a person looks at the image of an object in a mirror he notices that it appears the wrong way round; it is said to be **laterally inverted**. Figure 14.9 shows how this comes about. If L and R represent the left and right sides of the object viewed directly, it will be seen that L', the image of L, appears on the right side of the image in the mirror.

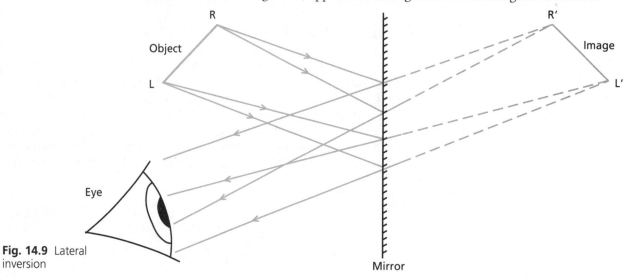

Fig. 14.9 Lateral inversion

Summary

1   Light normally travels in straight lines. This results in the formation of shadows and eclipses when an object is in a beam of light.

2   When a ray of light is reflected at a surface such as a mirror the angle of reflection equals the angle of incidence.

Chapter 15

Refraction of light

The laws of refraction are:

1. **The incident and refracted rays are on opposite sides of the normal at the point of incidence and all three are in the same plane.**
2. **The ratio of the sine of the angle of incidence to the sine of the angle of refraction is a constant.**

15.1 Refraction at a plane boundary

The refraction of rays of light can be studied using a ray box. We will consider what occurs when a single ray of light strikes a plane air to glass boundary (Fig. 15.1).

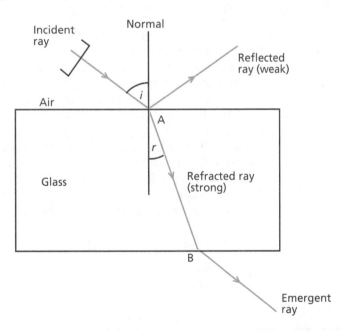

Fig. 15.1 Refraction at a plane boundary

The glass block stands on a sheet of white paper. A line at right angles to the boundary to be used is constructed near the middle of the face (a normal). It is arranged that the single ray strikes the glass block at *A* at various angles of incidence, *i*, in turn. The position of this ray and the emerging ray in each case are marked on the paper with dots. The angle of refraction *r*, within the block, is constructed by joining the points *AB* for each ray. The angle *r* is measured and, in each case, found to be less than the corresponding value of *i*; that is the ray always bends towards the normal.

Another example of refraction at a plane surface takes place in a prism (Fig. 15.2).

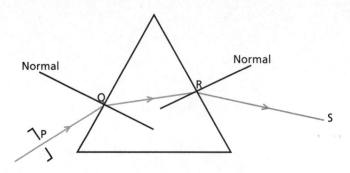

Fig. 15.2 Refraction by a prism

When light enters the glass prism at Q, its velocity is reduced and refraction takes place towards the normal. The reverse takes place at R as the light leaves the prism. In the case of a rectangular glass block, the refracting faces are parallel, and the emerging ray is parallel to the incident ray. For a prism the refracting faces are not parallel and this results in the emerging ray not being parallel to the incident ray. The angle between these two rays is called **the angle of deviation**. If the incident light is not all of the same wavelength, but a mixture, different wavelengths will undergo slightly different deviations at each face. Thus, for example, blue light will be deviated through a greater angle than red light.

A spectrum is obtained if a parallel beam of white light falls on a prism in the direction PQ (Fig. 15.2) and a screen is placed on the far side of the prism. The separate colours are visible in order from red to violet, red being the least deviated. However, the spectrum is not very good: a pure spectrum is obtained if a converging lens is added on the far side of the prism such that the screen passes through the focal point of the lens. This lens then focuses the parallel rays of the different colours which leave the prism; each colour to one place on the screen.

15.2 Internal reflection and critical angle

When light passes from one medium to a more optically dense medium (i.e. the speed of the light is reduced) refraction occurs for all angles of incidence, together with a very small amount of reflection. But refraction does not always occur at the surface of a less optically dense medium, for example when light is passing from glass or water to air.

Consider a ray passing from glass or water to air with a small angle of incidence (Fig. 15.3(a)). Here we get both a refracted and a reflected ray, the latter being relatively weak. If the angle of incidence is gradually increased the reflected ray becomes stronger and the refracted ray weaker, until for a certain **critical angle of incidence c**, the angle of refraction is 90°. This special case is shown in Fig. 15.3(b).

Since it is impossible to have an angle of refraction greater than 90°, it follows that all the light is internally reflected for angles of incidence greater than the critical angle. There is no refracted ray and this condition is known as **total internal reflection** (Fig. 15.3(c)).

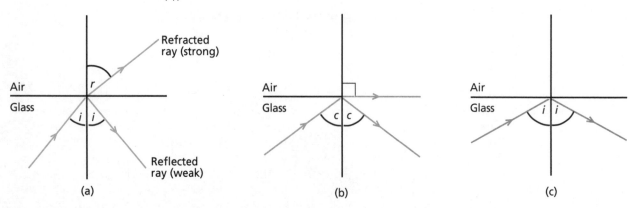

Fig. 15.3 (a) Refraction; (b) critical angle; (c) total internal reflection

The value of the critical angle for a glass to air boundary is about 42° and for water to air about 48°.

15.3 Refraction at a spherical boundary

Refraction of light at a spherical surface follows the same rules as refraction at a plane surface; that is:

① The incident and refracted rays are on opposite sides of the normal at the point of incidence and all three are in the same plane.

② The ratio of the sine of the angle of incidence to the sine of the angle of refraction is a constant.

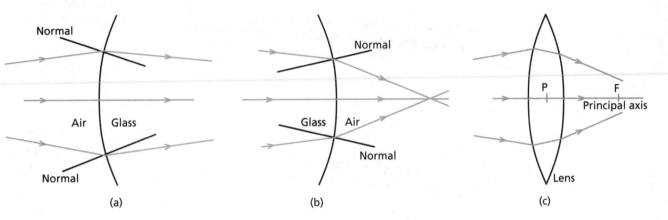

Fig. 15.4 Refraction at lens surfaces

Consider Fig. 15.4(a) showing three rays passing from air to glass. The three rays are all refracted according to the rules just stated; however, in this case, refraction results in the rays being brought together or focused. If the rays leave the glass, through a second boundary curved the other way, before they have come together, further focusing occurs (Fig. 15.4(b)), as they bend away from the normal. The combined effect of the two surfaces is to provide us with a converging lens as shown in Fig. 15.4(c).

The point **F** is the point through which rays incident parallel to the principal axis pass after refraction by the lens. It is called the **focal point** or **principal focus** of the lens. The distance **PF** is known as the **focal length** f.

The power of the lens is defined by

$$\textbf{power} = \frac{1}{f}$$

and if f is measured in metres the unit of power is called a dioptre.

The behaviour of a diverging lens is shown in Fig. 15.5. The point **F** is the point from which rays incident parallel to the principal axis appear to come after refraction by the lens. It is called the *focal point* of the lens. The distance **PF** is known as the **focal length** f. Because the rays do not actually pass through the focal point F it is virtual and the focal length f is therefore negative. The power is calculated in the same way as for a converging lens, but because f is negative, the power is also negative.

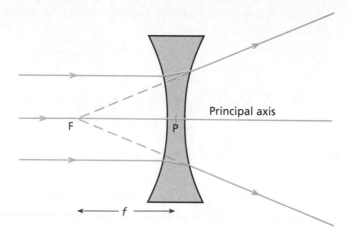

Fig. 15.5 Diverging lens

15.4 To determine the focal length of a converging (convex) lens

The focal length may be measured accurately by placing a plane mirror behind the lens and an illuminated point object in front of it (Fig. 15.6). The object O is moved until a clear image I of it is obtained alongside, due to reflection at the plane mirror. The distance PO is the focal length f.

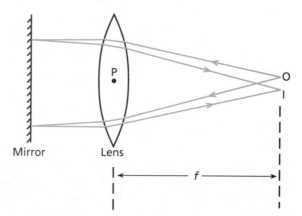

Fig. 15.6 Plane mirror method for determining the focal length of a convex lens

As the image occurs almost at the same point as the object, the light must return from the mirror almost along its incident path. This means that the light strikes the mirror normally; the light incident on the lens from the mirror is thus parallel with the principal axis.

An approximate value for the focal length of a converging lens may be found by casting the image of a distant object, such as the laboratory window in strong daylight, on a screen and measuring the distance between the lens and the screen.

15.5 Construction of ray diagrams

An image of a point on an object is formed where two rays from that point intersect after refraction. When constructing diagrams for converging lenses it is usually simplest to use any two of the following three rays:

❶ A ray parallel to the principal axis which passes through the focal point after refraction.

2 A ray through the focal point which emerges parallel to the principal axis after refraction.

3 A ray through the centre of the lens which is undeviated.

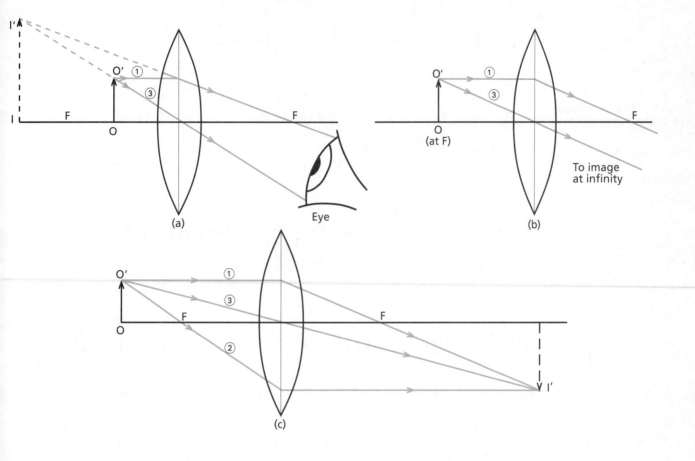

Fig. 15.7 Ray diagrams for a converging lens

Ray diagrams are most conveniently drawn to scale on squared paper. The height chosen for the object does not matter as the height of the image will always be in proportion. Figure 15.7 gives a series of diagrams to show the type of image formed for different distances of an object from a converging lens. In all cases the magnification is given by:

$$\text{magnification} = \frac{\text{height of image}}{\text{height of object}} = \frac{II'}{OO'}$$

$$\text{magnification} = \frac{\text{image distance}}{\text{object distance}}$$

When constructing ray diagrams for diverging lenses it is usually simplest to use any two of the following three rays:

1 A ray parallel to the principal axis which appears to come from the focal point *F* after refraction.

2 A ray incident in the direction of the focal point which emerges parallel to the principal axis after refraction.

3 A ray through the centre of the lens which is undeviated.

Figure 15.8 shows the formation of an image by a diverging lens. For all positions of the object the image is virtual, erect and smaller than the object, and is situated between the object and the lens.

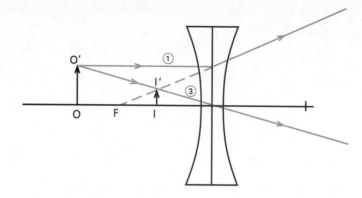

Fig. 15.8 Ray diagram for a diverging lens

For both converging and diverging lenses it can be shown that:

$$\frac{1}{u} + \frac{1}{v} = \frac{1}{f}$$

where
u = object distance from lens
v = image distance from lens
f = focal length of lens

Virtual distances carry a negative sign, including the focal lengths of diverging lenses.

15.6 Simple microscope (magnifying glass)

Figure 15.7(a) illustrates the use of a lens as a magnifying glass. Suppose that, without the lens, I is the closest to the eye that the object could normally be placed for clear focusing. Using the lens the object may now be placed at O and still be seen clearly as, to the eye, the object appears to be at I. The lens has thus enabled the object to be placed closer to the eye than would be the case without it, and the object appears larger because it appears to be closer.

15.7 The camera

The camera consists of a lens and light-sensitive film mounted in a light-tight box.
The distance of the lens from the film may be adjusted using the focusing ring.
This is marked in metres to show the distance at which an object will give a clear image. The amount of light entering the camera is controlled by a diaphragm of variable aperture (hole size) and the speed of the shutter. These used together allow the correct amount of light to reach the film and give the right exposure. The main features are shown in Fig. 15.9.
The ray diagram for a camera is shown in Fig. 15.7(c).

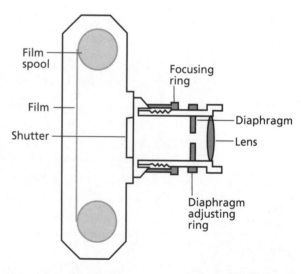

Fig. 15.9 Camera

15.8 The eye

A simplified diagram of the human eye is shown in Fig. 15.10. In many ways the eye is similar to the camera. An image is formed by the lens on the sensitive retina at the back of the eye.

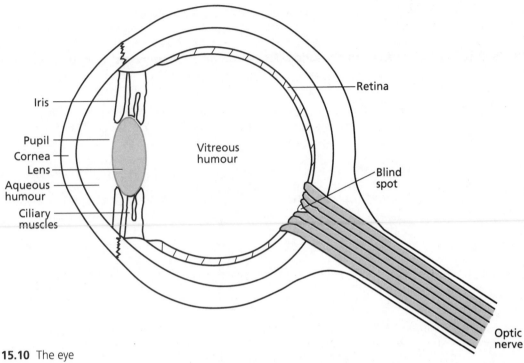

Fig. 15.10 The eye

The iris automatically adjusts the size of the circular opening in its centre, known as the pupil, according to the brightness of the light falling on it. Focusing of the image on the retina is achieved partly by refraction at the curved surface as light enters the eye, and partly by the action of the lens. The ciliary muscles vary the thickness of the lens and hence its focal length. When the muscles are relaxed the lens is thin. Unlike the camera, the position of the lens does not alter.

If the ciliary muscles weaken, the eye lens cannot be made sufficiently fat to clearly focus close objects. However, distant objects can be clearly focused. The eye is said to suffer from **long sight**. The same defect occurs if the eyeball is too short, and it may be corrected by using spectacles containing a converging lens (Fig. 15.11(a)). In the case of **short sight** the muscles do not relax sufficiently and consequently distant objects are focused in front of the retina. Short sight also occurs if the eyeball is too long. The defect can be corrected with a diverging lens (Fig. 15.11(b)).

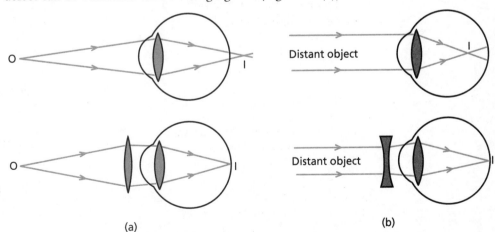

Fig. 15.11 Eye defects and their correction:
(a) long sight;
(b) short sight

In the case of long sight bifocal spectacles are frequently worn. Each eyepiece is in two halves, the upper half often being a plane sheet of glass through which to look at distant objects and the lower half being a converging lens through which to view close objects, such as a book or newspaper. Such an arrangement removes the necessity to be continually removing and replacing spectacles.

Summary

1   When light enters a different material its speed changes. This results in a change in its direction of motion (refraction) unless it crosses the boundary between the two materials at 90°. For example, when a ray of light enters glass from air it bends towards the normal. On leaving it bends away from the normal.

2   The focal point F of a lens is the point through which rays incident parallel to the principal axis pass after refraction by the lens. The distance between F and the centre of the lens is known as the focal length f.

3   The power of a lens $= \dfrac{1}{f}$ where f is in metres and the power in dioptres.

4   A converging lens bends rays of light inwards (towards the principal axis). Its focal length is positive. A diverging lens bends them away. Its focal length is negative.

5   For any lens

$$\frac{1}{u} + \frac{1}{v} = \frac{1}{f}$$

where u is the distance the object is away from the lens and v the distance the image is away from the lens. Real distances are treated as positive, virtual distances as negative.

6   Long sight occurs if the eye lens cannot be made sufficiently fat to clearly focus close objects or the eyeball is too short.

7   Short sight occurs if the eye lens cannot be made sufficiently thin to clearly focus distant objects or the eyeball is too long.

Chapter 16

The wave behaviour of light

16.1 Diffraction

The **diffraction** or spreading out which occurs when waves pass through a narrow gap or round a narrow object has already been mentioned in Chapter 13 in terms of water waves. It was then stated that the size of the gap or object had to be about the same as the wavelength of the waves, if significant bending was to occur. Light has a wavelength (about 5×10^{-7} m) very much less than the wavelength of water waves. The dimensions of the gap or object must be very small therefore if diffraction of light is to be observed. In practice a slit which is sufficiently narrow for the purpose can be made by drawing a sharp razor blade across the surface of a blackened microscope slide.

If the slide is held close to the eye and a light filament viewed through the slit, the filament looks much broader than it does with the naked eye, thus showing that light has been diffracted round the edges of the slit. The effect is most obvious if the filament and slit are parallel to each other. A similar effect can be obtained by partially closing your eyes, until there is a narrow slit between the eyelids, and then looking at a light.

16.2 Interference

Figure 16.1 shows a simple arrangement (Young's slits) to demonstrate the **interference** of light.

S_1 and S_2 are two slits marked on a microscope slide. If interference between light passing through the two slits is to be observed they should be 0.5 mm or less apart. They are illuminated by bright light from a lamp placed behind the single slit S; the purpose of the single slit being to cut out as much stray light as possible. The interference effect, in the form of light and dark fringes (Fig. 16.1), is observed on a screen placed a metre or so from the slits.

At certain places on the screen the light waves from the two slits will be in step (Fig. 13.8(a)), and bright fringes are seen. This occurs for places on the screen which are one, two, three, etc, wavelengths further from one slit than the other, or where there is no path difference (central bright fringe). These places correspond to the directions in Fig. 13.7 where the water waves reinforce.

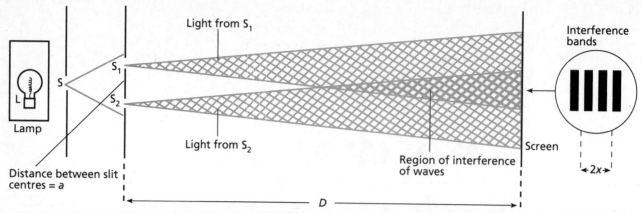

Fig. 16.1 Interference of light waves – Young's experiment

Waves from the slits arriving at places on the screen about midway between the bright fringes will be completely out of step. These places are one, three, five, etc, half wavelengths further from one slit than the other, and correspond to the directions of calm water in Fig. 13.7.

If the slits in Fig. 16.1 are drawn closer together the fringes on the screen are more spread out and vice versa. If the lamp used produces white light, which is a mixture of wavelengths, fringes for the different colours will occur at slightly different positions on the screen. The centre fringe will be white but colours will be seen after two or three fringes to either side of this.

The equation $x = \dfrac{\lambda D}{a}$ connects the distances shown in Fig. 16.1, where x is the fringe separation, D the distance between the plane of the slits and the screen, a the separation of the slits and λ the wavelength of the light used.

16.3 Polarization

Light travels by means of transverse waves. A beam of light (and all other parts of the electromagnetic spectrum) consists of electric and magnetic fields which vibrate at right angles to the direction of travel of the light. There are many such vibrations in the beam each at 90° to the direction of travel. When light passes through certain materials, called polaroids, all the vibrations are absorbed except those in one plane. This effect is called **polarization** and the light is said to be **polarized**.

Light is also polarized when it is reflected. After reflection the vibrations are mainly in one plane. Some sunglasses are made of polarizing material. These cut down the amount of light passing through them by absorbing all the vibrations except those in one plane. In particular they cut down glare by absorbing most of the light reflected by snow and the sea, for example, which has been polarized by reflection.

16.4 The electromagnetic spectrum

The light waves discussed in recent pages are just one small part of a family of waves called the **electromagnetic spectrum**. This family includes radio and television waves, infrared rays, light, ultraviolet light, X-rays and γ-rays. All members travel with a velocity of 3×10^8 m/s in space. Their difference lies in their frequency and wavelength. Radio waves lie at the long wavelength–low frequency end of the spectrum and γ-rays at the short wavelength–high frequency end. Because of their differing frequencies and wavelengths, different regions of the spectrum exhibit different properties. Some of these properties are summarized in Table 16.1.

Radio waves form the basis of all long distance 'wireless' communication. The behaviour of these waves is determined largely by the presence round the Earth of the ionosphere. This region of ionized gas, at heights between 80 and 400 km above the Earth's surface, acts as a mirror for radio waves of many frequencies. Waves of long wavelength and low frequency are reflected by this layer and such waves are thus very useful for communications round the Earth's surface. Waves of short wavelength and high frequency (>30 MHz) are able to penetrate the ionosphere and are used for all communications with artificial satellites. Radio waves can pass comparatively easily through brickwork and concrete.

Table 16.1

Wavelength (λ(m))	Type	Production	Reflection	Refraction	Diffraction and interference
>10^{-4}	Radio	Electrons oscillating in wires	Ionosphere	Atmosphere	Two stations
$7 \times 10^{-7} \rightarrow 10^{-4}$	Infrared	Hot objects	Metal sheet		
$4 \times 10^{-7} \rightarrow 7 \times 10^{-7}$	Visible	Very hot objects	Metal sheet	Glass	Grating
$10^{-9} \rightarrow 4 \times 10^{-7}$	Ultraviolet	Arcs and gas discharges			
$10^{-12} \rightarrow 10^{-8}$	X-rays	Electrons hitting metal targets			Crystals
<10^{-10}	γ-rays	Radioactive nuclei			

Any object heated nearly to red heat is a convenient source of infrared radiation. The radiation is readily absorbed (and also emitted) by objects with rough black surfaces, but strongly reflected by light polished ones. This radiation may therefore readily be detected by painting the bulb of a thermometer black and allowing the radiation to fall on the bulb. The thermometer reading rises.

Radiation with wavelengths just shorter than that of the violet end of the visible spectrum is termed ultraviolet radiation. It is emitted by any white hot body, such as the filament of an electric light bulb. However, in this case the radiation is absorbed by the glass envelope of the bulb. A discharge tube containing mercury vapour (with a quartz envelope) is a more intense source of ultraviolet radiation. A great deal of ultraviolet radiation is emitted by the Sun, but the majority of this is absorbed by the Earth's atmosphere and only a small fraction reaches the surface of the Earth. It is this which causes browning of the skin. One of the best known properties of ultraviolet radiation is its ability to cause substances to **fluoresce**. This is the term given to the emission of visible light by substances when ultraviolet radiation is shone on them. Examples are real diamonds, uranyl salts and paraffin oil.

The X-ray region of the electromagnetic spectrum is defined more by the method of generation of the radiation than by its precise wavelength. The method used is to cause electrons to hit a metal target. X-rays are used in medicine. Their ability to penetrate matter depends on the atomic number (see Unit 24.2) of the nuclei of the material through which they pass. X-rays are comparatively easily absorbed by bone which contains calcium (Z = 20), whereas they pass much more readily through organic material which contains hydrogen (Z = 1) and carbon (Z = 6). In addition, X-rays affect a photographic plate in a similar manner to visible light. An X-ray photograph may therefore be taken of the human leg, for example, and a bone fracture detected. X-rays are dangerous in too intense quantities. They eject electrons from the region on which they fall and can cause damage to living cells. In controlled quantities they can be used to kill off diseased tissue. X-rays like other forms of electromagnetic radiation show diffraction effects. The atomic spacing in crystals is comparable with the wavelength of X-rays, and thus X-rays are appreciably diffracted by atoms in crystals. The development of the science of X-ray crystallography has led to a much more detailed understanding of the structure of materials.

γ-rays are distinguished from X-rays in that they are emitted by the nuclei of natural or artificial radioactive materials. They are generally more penetrating, more dangerous and more difficult to screen than X-rays. They are mentioned in more detail in the unit on radioactivity (Unit 24.4).

Summary

1   Diffraction is the spreading out which occurs when light waves pass through a narrow gap or round a narrow object. The width of the gap or object should be equal to or smaller than the wavelength of the light if spreading out is to be significant.

2   When two sets of waves meet interference occurs. Where two crests or two troughs meet a large crest or trough results. Light is seen in these regions. Where a crest and a trough meet cancellation occurs and no light is seen. Such regions are dark.

3   In Young's experiment light from one lamp passes through two narrow slits which are close together. The diffraction which occurs at the slits results in the light overlapping beyond the slits and interference occurs.

Chapter 17
Sound

Sound waves differ from waves of the electromagnetic spectrum in that they are mechanical waves requiring a medium through which to pass. This may be demonstrated by placing an electric bell inside a glass jar from which the air can be removed (Fig. 17.1).

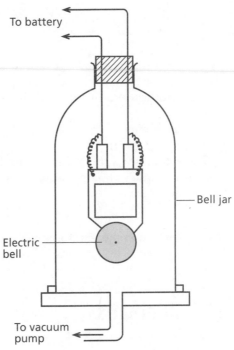

To battery

Bell jar

Electric
bell

To vacuum
pump

Fig. 17.1 Passage of
sound

When all the air has been pumped from the jar the ringing can no longer be heard, although the hammer can still be seen striking the gong. The faint vibration which is still audible comes from the passage of sound through the connecting wires.

Sound waves travel through solids and liquids as well as gases. If one person places his ear near a long metal fence while a second person gives the fence a tap some distance away two sounds will be heard. The first is due to transmission through the fence; the second comes through the air. Sound travels about 15 times faster through a solid than through air. Fishermen are using transistor 'bleepers' which, when lowered into the sea, attract fish up to one mile away. The speed of sound in water is about 1400 m/s.

Sound waves are **longitudinal** rather than transverse; that is the wave particles oscillate in the same direction as the wave travels and not at right angles to it. Owing to their longitudinal nature sound waves consist of a series of **compressions** and **rarefactions**.

Figure 17.2 shows how a vibrating tuning fork sends out a sound wave. The prongs are set vibrating by striking the fork. When the right-hand prong moves to the right it pushes the layers of air in that direction to the right. These layers are thus pushed closer together; that is, they are compressed. This disturbance is transmitted from one layer of particles to the next with the result that a compression pulse or high pressure region moves away from the fork. Similarly, when the prong moves to the left, a low pressure region or rarefaction occurs to its right. Compressions and rarefactions move alternately through the air. The particle at the centre of a compression is moving through its rest position in the same direction as the wave, whilst a particle at the centre of a rarefaction is moving through its rest position in the opposite direction to the wave. At regular intervals in the material through which the sound is travelling, there will be particles undergoing exactly the same movement at the same moment. Such particles are said to be **in phase**.

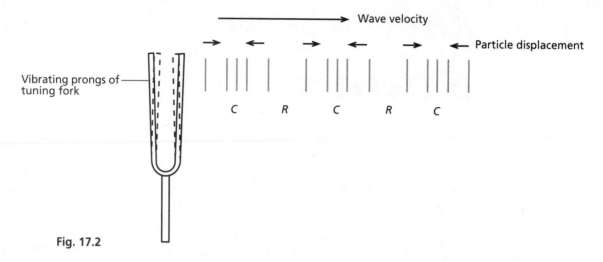

Fig. 17.2

As in the case of transverse waves, the distance between two successive particles in the same phase is called the **wavelength** λ.

The **amplitude** a of a wave is the maximum displacement of a particle from its rest position.

The **frequency** f is the number of complete oscillations made in one second. The unit is the hertz (Hz).

The **velocity** v is the distance moved by the wavefront in one second.

As in the case of transverse waves, the velocity, frequency and wavelength are related by the equation:

$$v = f\lambda$$

which is proved in the unit on progressive waves (see Unit 13.1).

17.1 Echoes

Echoes are produced by the reflection of sound from a hard surface such as a wall or cliff. Sound obeys the same laws of reflection as light. Thus if a person claps his hands, when standing some distance from a high wall, he will hear a reflection some time later. In order that the reflection may be heard separately from the original clap it must arrive at least 1/10 s later. As the speed of sound in air is 340 m/s, this means that the wall must be at least 17 m away.

Echoes may be used to measure the speed of sound in air reasonably accurately. One person should make the sound and another carry out the timing. The first person claps his hands and listens for the echo from a wall. For accurate results the time interval will need to be about half a second; thus he needs to be about 100 m from the wall. Having obtained an estimate of the time interval, he continues to clap his hands and adjust the rate of striking until each clap coincides in time with the arrival of the echo of the previous clap. When the correct rate of striking has been achieved the second person times 30 or more intervals between claps with a stopwatch. The speed of sound is then calculated by dividing the distance to the wall and back by the interval between two successive claps. The experiment should be repeated several times and an average value calculated.

17.2 Pitch

The **pitch** of a note depends on its frequency relative to other notes. This can be demonstrated by connecting a signal generator to a loudspeaker. If the frequencies 120, 150, 180 and 240 Hz (that is a ratio of 4:5:6:8) are produced in quick succession, the familiar sequence doh, me, soh, doh will be recognized. However, the same familiar sequence is noted when the frequencies 240, 300, 360 and 480 Hz are produced one after the other. The musical relation between notes thus depends on the ratio of their frequencies rather than their actual frequencies. An octave is always in the ratio 1:2.

17.3 Intensity and loudness

The most important factor affecting the **intensity** of a sound of given frequency is its **amplitude**. The intensity depends on the square of the amplitude and thus if the amplitude is doubled the intensity increases by a factor of four. Intensity is a measure of energy.

The **loudness** of a sound will obviously depend on its intensity. However, it also depends on the sensitivity of the human ear to sounds of different frequency. Loud sounds cause a greater pressure change on an eardrum than soft sounds. In normal conversation an eardrum will experience a pressure change of about one newton per metre squared (1 N/m^2 or 1 pascal), which is very small compared with atmospheric pressure (100 000 pascal).

Loud noises can cause pressure changes of about 100 pascal. These sounds are painful and can damage the eardrum. Laws now limit the noise level from industrial machinery, aeroplanes and discos. Double glazing and insulating panels made of material which traps many small pockets of air help to reduce noise levels. People who work with noisy machinery are required to wear ear-protectors.

17.4 Quality

A piano note can be distinguished from a trumpet note of the same pitch and loudness. The property which distinguishes them is known as **quality** or **timbre**. Musical instruments emit not only the basic or **fundamental** note but also **overtones**. An overtone (or harmonic) is a multiple of the fundamental frequency. Different instruments emit varying quantities of different overtones and it is the quantity of each present which determines the quality of the note. The note from the trumpet possesses a quality derived from the presence of strong overtones of high frequency.

17.5 Resonance

Resonance occurs when a vibrator is forced to vibrate at its own natural frequency. A car or washing machine may vibrate quite violently at a particular speed. When this occurs, the frequency of a rotating part is equal to the natural frequency of the body of the car or washing machine. When resonance occurs the maximum amount of energy is transferred from the forcing vibrator (motor, wheel or drum) to the driven vibrator (the body of the car or washing machine) and the amplitude of the vibrations of the driven vibrator greatly increases.

Summary

1   Sound is a longitudinal wave motion.

2   The equation $v = f\lambda$ applies (see Unit 13.1).

3   Sound is reflected according to the same rules as light. Reflected sound is often called an echo.

4   The pitch of sound depends on its frequency.

5   The intensity of sound is a measure of energy and depends on the square of the amplitude of the sound wave.

Chapter 18
Magnets

Certain materials have the property to attract iron; this property is known as **magnetism**. One such material is an iron ore called lodestone or magnetite; others are iron, steel, cobalt and nickel. Recently various alloys have been produced which can be made into very strong magnets. Alni, alcomax and ticonal are alloys of nickel and cobalt which are used for making powerful permanent magnets. Mumetal is an alloy which has been developed for the electromagnet and transformer, in which temporary magnets are used.

When a bar magnet is placed on a cork floating on water, so that it can swing in a horizontal plane, it comes to rest with its axis approximately in the north–south direction. The vertical plane in which the magnet lies is called the **magnetic meridian**. The end which points towards the north is called the north-seeking pole, or the N pole for short, and the other end the south-seeking or S pole.

If the N pole of a second magnet is brought near the N pole of the magnet on the floating cork, repulsion occurs and the cork and magnet tend to swing round. Repulsion occurs between two S poles in a similar way. However, an N and an S pole attract one another. These results may be summed up by saying:

Like poles repel, unlike poles attract

18.1 Making magnets

Magnetization by an electrical method is an efficient way of making magnets. A cylindrical coil is wound with about 500 turns of insulated copper wire and connected to a direct current supply (see Fig. 18.1). A coil of this kind is called a **solenoid**. A steel bar is placed inside the coil and the current switched on. The current creates a strong magnetic field within the coil and the steel immediately becomes a magnet, retaining its magnetism when the current is switched off.

A magnet may be demagnetized by placing it in the same coil but this time passing an alternating current through the coil. The magnet is slowly removed from the coil with the current still switched on.

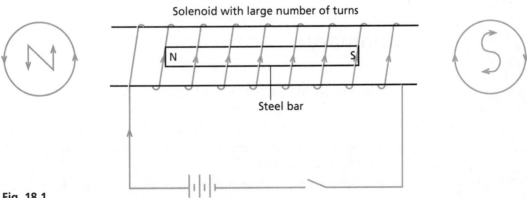

Fig. 18.1

18.2 Magnetic fields

In the space around a magnet a force is exerted on a piece of iron. This region is called a **magnetic field**. A magnetic field may be plotted by using a plotting compass to follow the lines of force. Figure 18.2 shows how this is done.

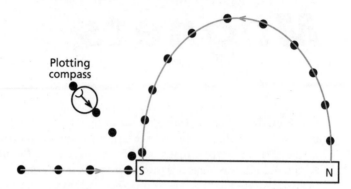

Fig. 18.2

A bar magnet is placed on a sheet of white paper. Starting near one end of the magnet, the positions of the ends of the compass needle are marked by pencil dots. The compass is then moved until the near end of the needle is exactly over the dot furthest from the magnet and a third dot made under the other end of the needle. This process is repeated many times until the compass reaches the other end of the magnet. Further lines of force may then be plotted in a similar way. Conventionally the lines of force are labelled with an arrow indicating the direction in which a north pole would move. The strength of the magnetic field in a particular region is indicated by the closeness of the lines of force.

A plotting compass is sensitive and can be used to plot relatively weak fields. It is unsuitable for fields in which the direction of the lines of force changes rapidly in a short distance, for example in the region of two magnets placed close together. These fields are best investigated using iron filings, although these do not indicate in which of the two possible directions the magnetic field is acting.

The magnets whose field is to be studied are placed beneath a sheet of stiff white paper. A thin layer of iron filings is then sprinkled from a caster. If the paper is tapped gently the filings form a pattern indicating the lines of force. Each filing becomes magnetized by induction and when the paper is tapped the filings vibrate and are able to turn in the direction of the magnetic force.

Figure 18.3 illustrates the magnetic field close to various arrangements of magnets. Figure 18.3(a) shows the magnetic field due to the Earth alone, while (b) shows the field due to a bar magnet alone. Figures 18.3(c) and (d) illustrate the fields resulting when a bar magnet is placed in the Earth's field. Figures 18.3(e) and (f) show the magnetic field resulting when two bar magnets are placed close together end to end. The points marked X are regions where the total field is zero. Such regions are called **neutral points**. The shape of the magnetic field round a bar magnet – Fig. 18.3(b) – is similar to that in the region of a solenoid through which an electric current is passing.

Summary

1   Some materials such as iron, steel, cobalt and nickel have the property to attract iron and are said to be magnetic.

2   A magnet has two poles, N and S. Unlike poles attract, whereas like poles repel.

3   In the space around a magnet a force is exerted on a piece of iron. This region is called a magnetic field.

4   A magnetic field is represented by lines with arrows on them. The arrows show the direction in which a N pole would move. Lines drawn close together represent a strong field.

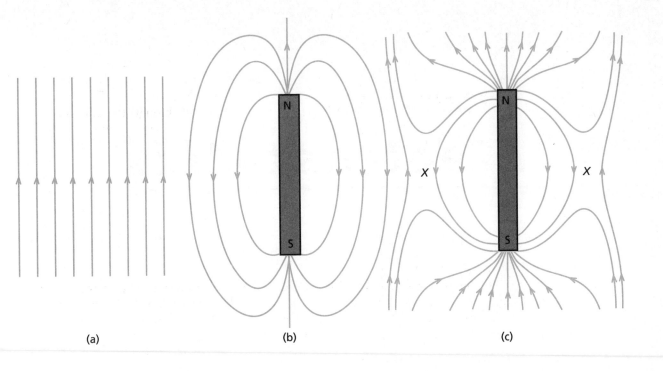

(a) (b) (c)

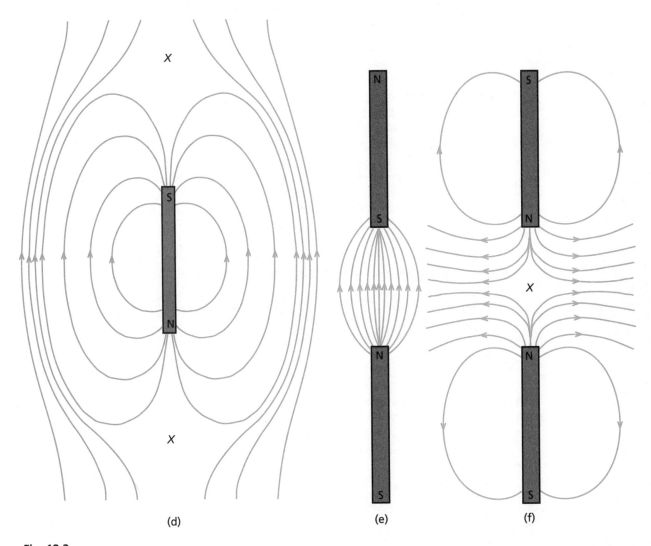

(d) (e) (f)

Fig. 18.3

Chapter 19
Electrostatics

If a rubber balloon is rubbed with a duster it will attract dust particles. Perspex, cellulose acetate and the vinyl compounds which were used for LPs (gramophone records) show the same attraction. This is because the materials have become charged with static electricity. Charging by friction is sometimes associated with a crackling sound. This is often heard when dry hair is combed or a terylene or nylon shirt is removed from the body. The crackling is caused by small electric sparks which may be seen if the room is in darkness.

If a rod is charged by rubbing and then touched on a small pith ball, the ball becomes charged. If two pith balls are suspended close to each other on nylon threads and charged from the same rod, they repel. However, if the balls are charged from two rods made of different materials they may attract each other. This behaviour indicates the presence of two types of static charge, referred to as **positive** and **negative** charge. It is found that **like charges repel and unlike charges attract**.

In experiments on static electricity the standard method for obtaining positive charge is to rub glass or cellulose acetate with silk. Negative charge is obtained on an ebonite rod by rubbing it with fur.

Glass, cellulose acetate, ebonite and polythene are examples of materials which are electrical insulators. That is, the charges produced on their surfaces do not move along or through the material, but remain at the spot where they are produced. If a piece of one of these materials is placed in an electric circuit, no current flows as the charge cannot pass through the piece of material.

Metals are examples of electrical conductors. Conductors can be charged by rubbing, for example by flicking fur across the cap of a gold-leaf electroscope. However, if a metal rod is held in the hand and rubbed, the charge formed flows through the metal and is lost to earth via the hand. If a piece of metal forms part of an electric circuit, the charge will pass through it and a current flows round the circuit. Some other materials conduct an electric charge but much less readily than metals. Only a very small current will pass round electric circuits containing such materials.

Summary

1   Like electrical charges repel, unlike charges attract.

2   An ebonite rod rubbed with fur, or a rubbed polythene strip, acquires a negative charge; a glass rod rubbed with silk or a rubbed cellulose acetate strip acquires a positive charge.

3   Metals, the human body and the earth are examples of conductors; glass, ebonite and plastics are normally insulators.

Chapter 20
Current electricity

All atoms possess small negatively charged particles called electrons. In the case of metals some of these electrons are very weakly attached to their atoms and can easily be detached and made to flow through the metal. Metals are therefore good conductors of electricity.

In a battery one plate is at a positive potential and the other plate is at a negative potential, this potential difference being a property of the chemicals of which the battery is made. If the battery terminals are joined by a length of wire, the potential difference which exists between the ends of the wire will result in the weakly bound electrons already mentioned flowing through the wire. This constitutes an electric current.

Before the nature of an electric current was fully understood, the direction chosen to indicate current was, unfortunately, from the positive plate to the negative, that is, opposite to the flow of electrons. This is known as the *conventional current* and is the one normally used.

When the rate of flow of a charge past a point is 6×10^{18} electrons per second, the current is 1 **ampere (A)**.

As an electric current is a flow of an electric charge, the quantity of electric charge which passes any point in a circuit will depend on the strength of the current and the time for which it flows. The unit of electric charge is the **coulomb**. **A coulomb is the quantity of electric charge conveyed in one second by a steady current of one ampere.**

Thus

$$\text{charge } (Q) = \text{ current } (I) \times \text{time } (t)$$

$$Q = It$$

20.1 Potential difference

In order to achieve current flow in a circuit a potential difference V must exist. The unit of potential difference is the **volt (V)**. **Two points are at a potential difference of one volt if one joule of work is done per coulomb of electricity passing between the points.**

20.2 Resistance

As the potential difference between the ends of a conductor is increased the current passing through it increases. **If the temperature of the conductor does not alter,** the current which flows is proportional to the potential difference applied (Ohm's law). Figure 20.1(a) shows this effect.

The gradient of this graph has a constant value, obtained by dividing the potential difference at any point by the current. The value of this constant gradient is known as the **resistance R** of the conductor. The unit of resistance is the **ohm (Ω)**.

$$\frac{V}{I} = \text{constant} \quad (R) \quad \text{(Ohm's law)}$$

hence $\qquad V = IR$

A good conductor is one with a low resistance, a poor one has a high resistance.

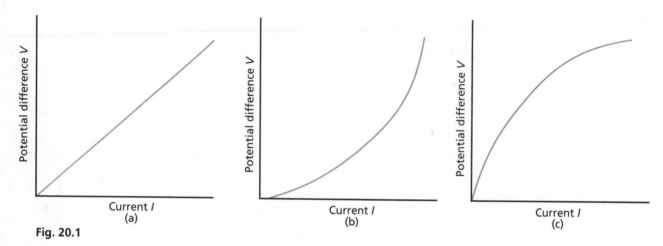

Fig. 20.1

In some conductors the current is not proportional to the potential difference between its ends. In a light bulb V/I is found to increase with temperature, that is R is not constant but increases as the temperature of the filament of the bulb increases. Figure 20.1(b) shows the relationship between potential difference and current in such cases.

Figure 20.1(c) shows results that might be obtained from a thermistor for which the resistance decreases with increasing temperature.

20.3 Ammeters and voltmeters

An **ammeter** is used to measure the electric current through a conductor and must be in series with the conductor. It has a resistance; however, this should be as small as possible so that it only reduces the current to be measured by a very small amount.

A **voltmeter** measures potential difference between two points in a circuit. It must be in parallel with the part of the circuit concerned. In order that it should take as little current as possible out of the main circuit it must have as large a resistance as possible.

Figure 20.2 shows an ammeter Ⓐ and a voltmeter Ⓥ correctly connected to determine the value of the resistance R.

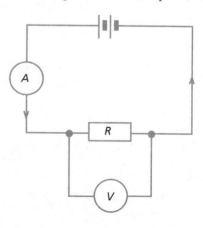

Fig. 20.2

20.4 Resistors

There are a wide variety of resistors. Filaments in lamps consist of a thin coiled length of tungsten wire, which glows white hot. The resistance of the filament is between about 500 and 1000 ohms depending on the power of the lamp. Hair dryers, irons, electric fires, electric kettles and hotplates have filaments made from nickel alloys such as nichrome. All these appliances have resistors of fixed value.

Sometimes it is essential to be able to vary the resistance in a circuit or in an electrical appliance. Variable resistors are used to vary the voltage output of power supplies, the brightness of lamps and televisions, and the sound volume of radios and televisions. The circuit symbol for a variable resistor is shown in Fig. 20.3.

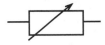

Fig. 20.3

20.5 Resistors in series

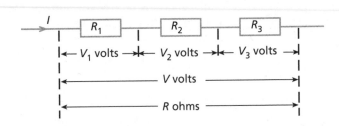

Fig. 20.4
Resistors in series

A number of **resistors** R_1, R_2, R_3, are said to be connected **in series** if they are connected end to end as shown in Fig. 20.4. The current I must be the same throughout the circuit as it has only one route to follow.

If R is the combined resistance of R_1, R_2, and R_3 and V is the total potential difference across them, then

$$V = IR$$

but V is the sum of the individual potential differences across R_1 R_2, and R_3. Thus

$$V = V_1 + V_2 + V_3$$

and

$$V = IR_1 + IR_2 + IR_3$$

therefore

$$IR = IR_1 + IR_2 + IR_3$$

and hence

$$\mathbf{R = R_1 + R_2 + R_3}$$

The same argument may be applied to any number of resistors in series.

In Fig. 20.2 the electromotive force E of the battery must not only provide the potential difference to drive the current through the resistors, but also through itself V_b. The battery is said to have its own resistance r, known as its **internal resistance**. The total resistance of the circuit must include r, and is equal to the sum of r, R_1 R_2 and R_3 (Fig. 20.4). Now

$$V = V_1 + V_2 + V_3$$

and

$$E = V_1 + V_2 + V_3 + V_b$$

hence

$$E - V = V_b$$

V_b is usually referred to as the *lost volts* in the circuit.

20.6 Resistors in parallel

Resistors are said to be **in parallel** when they are placed side by side in a circuit (Fig. 20.5).

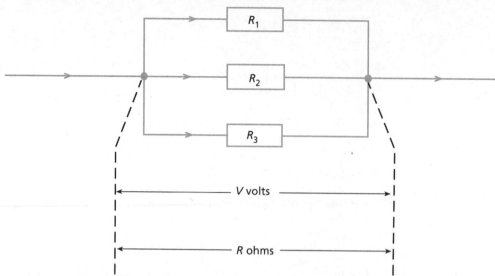

Fig. 20.5 Resistors in parallel

The conductance of each branch of the circuit is I/V, that is the quantity of current which passes for each volt of potential difference applied. But I/V is equal to $1/R$; thus the conductance of each branch of a circuit is the reciprocal of its resistance. The total conductance of the three resistors in parallel is clearly the sum of the conductance of each individual resistor, as each one provides the current in the circuit with an alternative route, and thus makes its passage easier.

$$\text{Thus} \quad \frac{1}{R} = \frac{1}{R_1} + \frac{1}{R_2} + \frac{1}{R_3}$$

The same argument may be applied to any number of resistors in parallel. As an example consider a 2-ohm resistor and a 4-ohm resistor in parallel with each other.

$$\frac{1}{R} = \frac{1}{2} + \frac{1}{4} = \frac{3}{4}$$

$$\text{Thus} \qquad R = \tfrac{4}{3} = 1\tfrac{1}{3}\,\Omega$$

The combined resistance of any number of resistors in parallel is always less than the value of any one of them. This is clear when one realizes that placing one resistor in parallel with another provides an alternative route for the current and thus eases its passage round the circuit.

20.7 Energy

When a potential difference is applied to the ends of a conductor some of the electrons inside it are set in motion by electric forces. Work is therefore done and the electrons acquire energy. The moving electrons form an electric current, and the energy of this current appears in various forms according to the type of circuit of which the conductor forms a part. For example in an electric fire the energy of the current is largely made available as heat, in an electric light as heat and light, and in an electric motor as mechanical energy of rotation. Energy in these various forms is produced at the expense of the source of electricity.

From the definition of the volt it can be seen that if a potential difference of one volt is applied to the ends of a conductor and one coulomb of electricity passes through it, then the work done, or energy transformed, is 1 joule. Hence if the potential difference applied is V volts and the quantity of electricity that passes is Q coulombs then the work done is QV joules.

However   Charge (Q) = current $(I) \times$ time (t)

or $Q = It$

therefore   work done $= QV = VIt$ joules

Two other expressions for the work done may be obtained by using Ohm's law. As

$$V = IR$$

$$\textbf{Work done} = VIt = I^2Rt = \frac{V^2t}{R}$$

20.8 Power

The definition of power, given in Unit 3.12, is the rate of doing work or transferring energy.

$$\text{Power} = \frac{\text{work done}}{\text{time taken}}$$

If the work done is measured in joules, the unit of power is the **watt (W)**. Using the equations for energy given in the last unit, power may be obtained by dividing by time.

$$\textbf{Power} = VI = I^2R = \frac{V^2}{R} \textbf{ watts} \qquad I^2R \qquad \frac{V^2}{R}$$

The first expression in words is:

$$\text{Power} = \text{potential difference} \times \text{current}$$

Example:
Find (a) the current taken by, and (b) the resistance of, the filament of a lamp rated at 240 V, 40 W.

$$\text{Power} = \text{potential difference} \times \text{current}$$

therefore $\text{current} = \dfrac{\text{power}}{\text{potential difference}}$

$$= \frac{40}{240} = \frac{1}{6} = 0.16 \text{ A}$$

but   potential difference = current $\times$ resistance

thus $\text{resistance} = \dfrac{\text{potential difference}}{\text{current}}$

$$= \frac{240}{1/6} = 1440 \text{ }\Omega$$

In the case of a lamp only a small proportion (about 20%) of the electrical energy transformed becomes light; the remainder (about 80%) becomes heat. The lamp is thus about 20% efficient. Because it works in a different way a fluorescent tube is about 80% efficient. In other words the same intensity of light can be obtained for about one quarter of the cost.

20.9 Cost

If an electricity meter is inspected it will be found to have the abbreviation 1 kWh on it. This stands for kilowatt-hour, the commercial unit of electrical energy. It is the energy supplied in one hour by a rate of working of 1000 W.

$$1 \text{ kilowatt-hour} = 1000 \text{ watt-hours}$$
$$= 1000 \text{ joules/second for 1 hour}$$
$$= 1000 \times 60 \times 60 \text{ joules}$$
$$= 3\,600\,000 \text{ joules or 3.6 MJ}$$

Example:

Find the cost of running a 2 kW fire for 3 hours if the cost of electrical energy is 6.0 pence per kilowatt-hour (unit).

$$\text{Total energy consumed} = \text{power} \times \text{time}$$
$$= 2 \times 3 \text{ kWh}$$
$$= 6 \text{ kWh}$$
$$\text{Cost} = 6 \times 6.0 = 36 \text{ pence}$$

20.10 House electrical installation

The cable bringing the mains electricity supply into a house contains two wires, one of which is 'live', and the other 'neutral'. The neutral wire is earthed at the local transformer substation, so it is at earth potential. At some convenient place inside the house the mains cable enters a sealed box, where the live wire is connected to the Electricity Board's fuse. On the far side of this box the power cable enters the meter and from there it goes to the main fuse box. The fuse box contains a separate fuse for each of the lighting circuits, ring circuit and cooker circuit (Fig. 20.6).

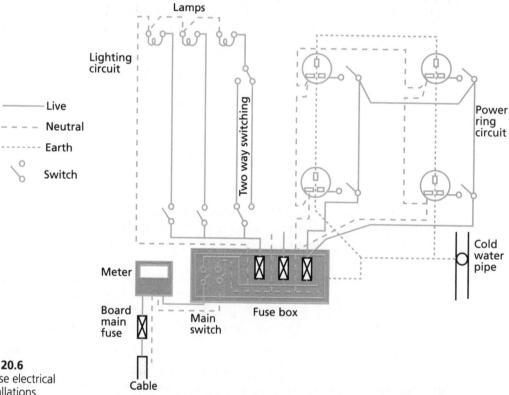

Fig. 20.6
House electrical installations

In modern installations the power sockets are tapped off a ring circuit. This cable passes through the various rooms in the house and has both its ends connected to the mains supply. Thus there are two paths by which the current may get to a particular socket, which effectively doubles the capacity of the cable.

It can be seen from Fig. 20.6 that all light and power switches and fuses are placed in the live side of the supply. If they were in the neutral side all light and power sockets would remain live when the switches were in the off position.

20.11 Circuit breakers

These are used in consumer units instead of fuses. There are two types. The first contains an electromagnet which, when the current exceeds the rated value of the circuit breaker, becomes sufficiently strong to separate a pair of contacts and breaks the circuit. The second type, the Residual Current Circuit Breaker, compares the currents in the live and neutral wires and, if they differ by even a small amount (indicating a leakage to earth), it throws open a switch which can be reset when the fault has been corrected.

20.12 Fuses

For safety reasons all domestic electrical appliances are fused. That is, in at least one place on each circuit, a fuse is fitted, which will 'blow' if a fault develops in the circuit and too great a current passes through it. This arrangement protects the wiring against the possibility of overheating and setting fire to the house.

The main house fuses for the different circuits generally consist of short lengths of tinned copper wire fitted into porcelain carriers. These fuses are usually situated under the stairs or in a cupboard which also contains the electricity meter and Electricity Board fuse.

In addition, items which are separately plugged into power sockets – for example, fires – contain a fuse in the plug. This type of fuse consists of a small glass cartridge with a thin wire through its centre. Such a fuse is rated at 2, 5, 10 or 13 A to suit the appliance to which it is connected. For example, the value of the fuse which should be used in the plug of a 240 V, 2 kW fire is calculated as follows.

$$\text{Power} = \text{voltage} \times \text{current}$$

thus $$2000 = 240 \times \text{current}$$

and the $$\text{current} = \frac{2000}{240}\,\text{A} = 8.33\,\text{A}$$

A 10 A fuse would thus be suitable.

If a fault develops in the appliance, the fuse in its plug will normally 'blow' rather than the larger one in the main fuse box. This avoids other appliances being put out of action at the same time.

The thickness of wire used in any fuse is such that it will overheat and melt if the current passing through it exceeds its specified rating by much. Once the wire has melted the circuit is broken.

When a fuse has 'blown' it is essential that the cause of the fuse blowing is found before it is repaired or replaced and the appliance used again. Sometimes a fuse 'blows' because the fuse wire is very old and has become weakened by oxidation, or it can blow due to a fault in the circuit, such as a short circuit in the flex where the insulation has worn and frayed. Whatever the fault it must be found and put right before a new fuse is fitted.

Two other types of fuse are worth mentioning. An **anti-surge** fuse is designed not to melt if there is a surge of current for a very short time but it is designed to melt if a large current flows for a longer time. A current surge often happens when a circuit is first switched on. A **quick blow** fuse does just what its name implies; it melts very quickly if a large current flows.

20.13 Earthing

Besides the live (brown) and neutral (blue) wires, all power circuits are provided with a third wire (green and yellow stripes) which has been earthed by a good electrical joint to the cold water supply. When an appliance is connected to the circuit the earth wire provides a low resistance route between the casing of the appliance and the earth. This is a safeguard to prevent anyone receiving a shock by touching the casing should this become 'live'. Such a danger would arise if the insulation on the live flex had become worn and allowed the live wire to come into contact with the casing of the appliance. If this happened in a properly earthed appliance, a large current would instantaneously flow to earth and the fuse would blow, thereby cutting off the supply.

Loose connections in plugs are another potential source of danger to the person. Proper earthing again removes the danger.

Parts of many modern appliances, such as the bases of electric lamps, are made from plastic. In such cases there is no need for an earth wire since plastic does not conduct electricity. This method of protection is called double insulation and is denoted by the sign ▣.

Summary

1   **Charge (Q) = current (I) × time (t).**

2   In order to achieve current flow a potential difference must exist. The unit of potential difference is the volt (V). Two points are at a potential difference of one volt if one joule (J) of work is done per coulomb of electricity passing between the points.

3   The resistance of a conductor is defined by the equation

$$\textbf{Resistance } (R) = \frac{\textbf{potential difference } (V)}{\textbf{current } (I)} \quad \text{(Ohm's law)}$$

   Current is measured in amperes (A) and resistance in ohms (Ω).

4   A good conductor has a low resistance and a poor conductor has a high resistance.

5   In a simple series circuit the current has the same value at all points round the circuit.

6   The total resistance R of a number of resistors R_1, R_2, R_3, in series is given by
$$R = R_1 + R_2 + R_3 \text{ etc.}$$

7   In a parallel circuit the total current entering a junction must equal the total current leaving it.

8   The total resistance R of a number of resistors R_1, R_2, R_3 all in parallel with each other is given by
$$\frac{1}{R} = \frac{1}{R_1} + \frac{1}{R_2} + \frac{1}{R_3} \text{ etc.}$$

9   The work done or energy transformed by the flow of an electric current is given by
$$\textbf{Work done} = VIt = I^2Rt = \frac{V^2t}{R}$$

10   Power is the rate of doing work or transforming energy
$$\textbf{Power} = \frac{\textbf{work done}}{\textbf{time taken}} = VI = I^2R = \frac{V^2}{R}$$

11   The fuse is the weakest point in a circuit. The fuse wire melts and breaks the circuit if more current flows than the circuit is designed to take. The fuse protects the appliance and the circuit from damage.

12   The earth wire provides a low resistance route between the casing of an appliance and earth. It prevents anyone receiving a shock by touching the casing should the casing become 'live'.

Chapter 21
Electromagnetism

Whenever an electric current flows in a conductor a magnetic effect is present in the region of the conductor. This can most easily be demonstrated by passing a current down a vertical conductor, such as a retort stand (Fig. 21.1).

At some convenient height the conductor passes through a hole in a horizontal platform. A number of small compasses are placed on the platform.

When the current is switched on the compass needles swing from pointing to magnetic north and re-align themselves in a circular path around the wire.

The influence of the current in the region of the wire is called a **magnetic field**.

This result can be remembered using the following rule. Imagine the wire to be grasped in the right hand with the thumb pointing along the wire in the direction of the current. The direction of the fingers will give the direction of the lines of force. This rule is purely an aid to memory; it does not explain how the lines occur.

A knowledge of the magnetic field around a straight conductor can be used to predict the pattern round other simple geometrical arrangements of current-carrying wires – for example, a flat coil and a solenoid.

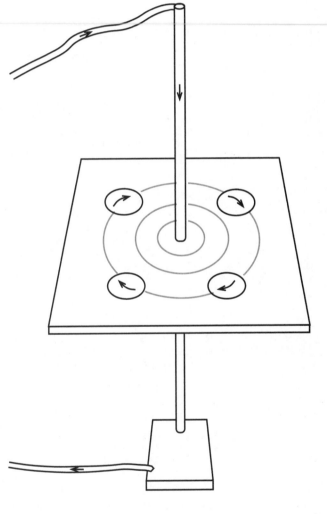

Fig. 21.1

The pattern of lines of force when a current is passed through a flat circular coil is shown in Fig. 21.2.

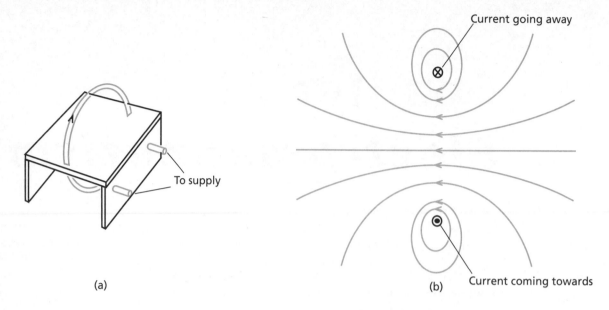

(a)

Current going away

(b)   Current coming towards

Fig. 21.2

Figure 21.3 illustrates the magnetic field due to a current in a solenoid.

If one considers the circular magnetic field round each short length of wire in the flat circular coil, it can be seen that the field adds up through the centre of the coil. This leads to a strong field through the coil but a weak one outside it (Fig. 21.2(b)). A solenoid may be considered as a series of flat circular coils, each a little spaced from one another on a common axis. Each turn of insulated wire gives a magnetic field similar to that of a flat circular coil. The fields between neighbouring turns oppose one another and cancel, but the fields along the common axis reinforce, producing the pattern shown in Fig. 21.3(b).

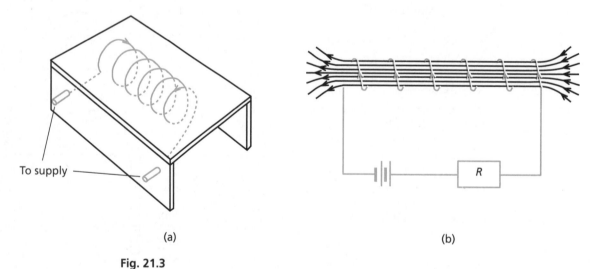

To supply

R

(a)   (b)

Fig. 21.3

The magnetic fields resulting from a current passing through flat coils and solenoids of square cross-sectional area are similar to those shown for circular areas.

21.1 The electromagnet

The use of a solenoid for making magnets has already been described in Unit 18.1. When a piece of steel is placed inside a solenoid and the current switched on, the steel becomes a magnet and remains one when the current is switched off. If a piece of soft-iron is used instead, the iron acts as a magnet only while the current is switched on. Figure 21.4(a) shows such an electromagnet. Sometimes the cores of electromagnets are U-shaped (Fig. 21.4(b)). This arrangement has the advantage that the attraction of both ends can be used simultaneously.

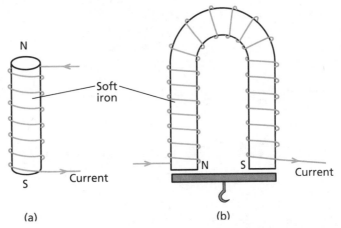

Fig. 21.4
Electromagnet

(a)   (b)

Electromagnets are very strong. A small one, made in a laboratory from a U-shaped core and a few turns of wire each carrying a current of a few amps, is capable of lifting several kilograms. Those used in industry can lift several tonnes, for example car and lorry bodies. Yet when the current is switched off, the magnetism ceases and the load is released.

21.2 The microphone

Sound waves cause the diaphragm of a microphone (Fig. 21.5) to move backwards and forwards. This varies the pressure on the carbon granules between the movable carbon dome attached to the diaphragm and the fixed carbon cup at the back. When the pressure increases, the granules are squeezed together thus lowering their electrical resistance; a decrease of pressure has the opposite effect. These changes in resistance cause the electric current to vary in the same way that the sound wave varies.

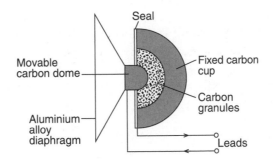

Fig. 21.5

21.3 The loudspeaker

Varying currents from the amplifier at the output of a radio or cassette player pass through a short cylindrical coil. The coil's turns are at right angles to the magnetic field of a magnet with a central pole and a surrounding ring pole (Fig. 21.6). Thus a force acts on the coil which makes it move in and out. The paper cone attached to the coil moves with it and sets up sound waves in the air around the loudspeaker.

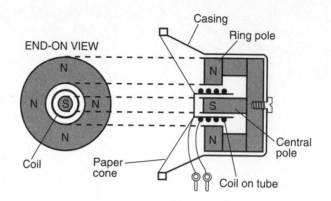

Fig. 21.6 A loudspeaker

21.4 The force on charges moving in a magnetic field

Figure 21.7 shows a current-carrying wire placed in a magnetic field. As soon as the current is switched on the length of wire *AB* moves horizontally on the other two pieces. The interaction of the magnetic field due to the current flow and that due to the magnets results in a horizontal force. The effect may be understood by reference to Fig. 21.8.

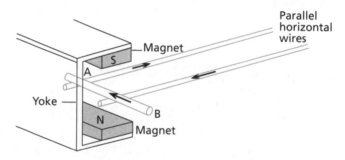

Fig. 21.7

The two fields shown separately in Figs. 21.8 (a) and (b) reinforce to the left and tend to cancel to the right of the wire when combined (Fig. 21.8(c)). A strong magnetic field results on the left with the lines in tension. The tension results in a force from left to right. If either magnetic field is reversed the force reverses.

It should be noted that the current, the magnetic field due to the magnets and the force produced are all three mutually at right angles. If the current is parallel to the field due to the magnets there is no force.

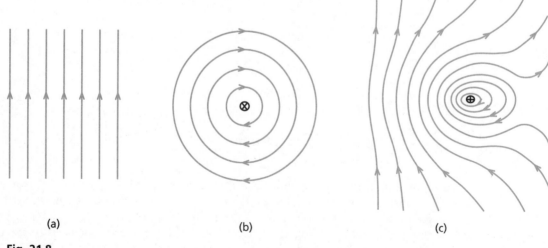

(a)   (b)   (c)

Fig. 21.8

If a stream of electric charges passes through a gas, as in a fine beam tube (Fig. 21.9), rather than a wire, the same force results. However, whereas in a wire the charges (electrons) are inhibited from moving by its stiffness, this is not so in a gas, where they are free to change their direction of motion as soon as the force acts. The force always remains at right angles to their direction of motion, as well as to the magnetic field, and so the charges move in the arc of a circle (see Unit 3.5).

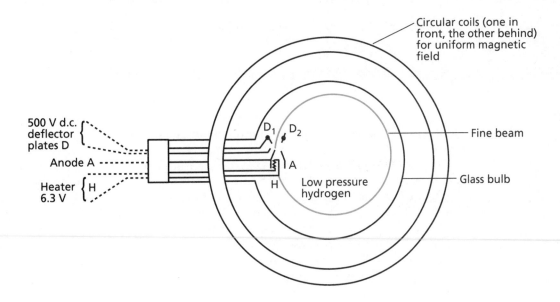

Fig. 21.9 Fine beam tube

21.5 The d.c. electric motor

Figure 21.10 shows the construction of a simple direct current (d.c.) electric motor. It

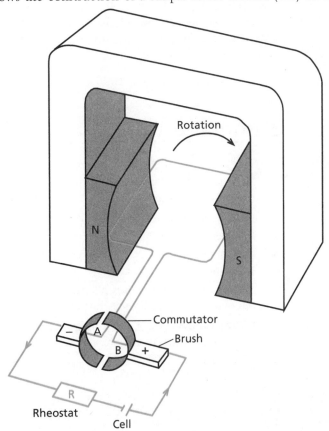

Fig. 21.10 Simple d.c. motor

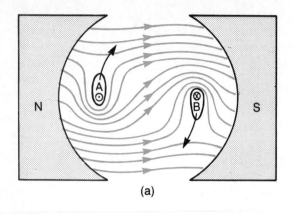

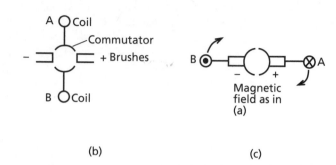

(a)   (b)   (c)

Fig. 21.11

consists of a rectangular coil of wire mounted on a spindle so that it is free to rotate between the pole pieces of a permanent magnet. The two ends of the coil are soldered to the two halves of a copper split ring or **commutator**, which is a device for reversing the direction of current flow in the coil every half revolution. The two brushes press lightly against the commutator. When a current is passed through the coil it rotates. Figure 21.11(a) shows a cross-section through the coil together with the resultant magnetic field, which is strong above the right side and also below the left side. The coil therefore rotates clockwise.

When the coil is vertical the brushes touch the space between the two halves of the commutator. There is no torque at this position (Fig. 21.11(b)); however, the coil's momentum carries it past the vertical, and when this has occurred the commutator halves automatically change contact from one brush to the other. This reverses the current through the coil (Fig. 21.11(c)) and thus it rotates through the next half turn. The reversal of the direction of current flow by the commutator each half turn ensures the continued rotation of the coil.

The simple motor described is not very efficient or powerful, as the torque changes from a maximum when the coil is horizontal to zero when it is vertical. The motor can be improved by winding a number of coils, each of many turns, at different angles round a soft-iron armature. The greater number of turns in a coil gives a greater torque; having a number of coils ranged at angles round the armature means that when one is vertical another is horizontal thus resulting in an even torque. The iron armature becomes magnetized and increases the magnetic field through the coils, resulting in a greater torque. It is also usual for the magnetic field to be provided by electromagnets rather than permanent magnets.

Summary

1   Whenever an electric current flows in a conductor a magnetic field is present in the region of the conductor.

2   The magnetic field round a coil carrying direct current is similar in shape to that round a bar magnet.

3   When a steel bar is placed in a coil carrying direct current the bar becomes permanently magnetized.

4   When a bar of soft iron is placed in a coil carrying direct current the soft iron becomes a strong magnet only while the current flows. This is an electromagnet.

5   Charges moving at 90° to a magnetic field experience a force at 90° to both their direction of motion and the direction of the magnetic field.

6   The behaviour described in point 5 is the basis of an electric motor.

Chapter 22
Electromagnetic induction

The magnetic field in a region is often referred to as **magnetic flux**.

22.1 Laws

1. **Faraday's. Whenever there is a change in the magnetic flux linked with a circuit an electromotive force is induced, the strength of which is proportional to the rate of change of the flux through the circuit.**
2. **Lenz's. The direction of the induced current is always such as to oppose the change producing it.**

The truth of these laws is best illustrated by considering a simple experiment. First a centre-zero meter is connected in series with a cell and a suitable high resistance, and the direction of movement of the pointer noted when a small current passes in a known direction. The meter is now connected to the ends of a straight wire placed at right angles to the lines of magnetic field between two opposite magnetic poles (Fig. 22.1).

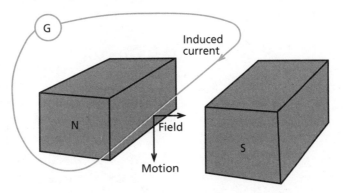

Fig. 22.1

If the wire is moved downwards the meter indicates that an induced current flows in the direction shown. If the wire is moved up the current flows in the opposite direction. The same results are obtained if the wire is held still and the magnets moved up or down, respectively. It is the relative motion between the wire and magnetic field which leads to the induced voltage and hence current. The quicker the relative motion takes place the greater the deflection (Faraday's law).

While the induced current flows there is a magnetic field around the wire. Consideration of the effect of this field and that of the magnets shows that it results in an upward force in Fig. 22.1. That is, the induced current leads to a force acting in the opposite direction to the movement of the wire and thus opposing it (Lenz's law).

22.2 The simple d.c. dynamo

The simple direct current electric motor described in Unit 21.5 may be used as a simple d.c. dynamo. The motor is connected in series with a resistance and a moving coil meter instead of a voltage source. When the coil is rotated the meter is seen to deflect in one direction, although the deflection is not a steady one. The commutator ensures that, although the current in the coil itself reverses during the second half of a rotation, the same brush always remains positive and the other negative.

The simple dynamo just described is not very efficient. A practical dynamo has a number of coils wound in slots cut in the armature. Each coil has its own pair of segments in a multi-segment commutator. This arrangement ensures that the e.m.f. obtained is fairly steady, as it is only the horizontal coils which are connected to the brushes at any given moment. The iron armature is built in layers, each one insulated from its neighbours. Although e.m.f.'s are induced in these layers of iron as they rotate in the magnetic field, very little current flows in the armature as a result, due to this insulation.

22.3 The simple a.c. dynamo

This differs from the simple d.c. version, described in Unit 22.2, only in its connections (Fig. 22.2). The ends of the coil are connected to two slip rings mounted on the coil spindle. One side of the coil is thus always connected to the same brush.

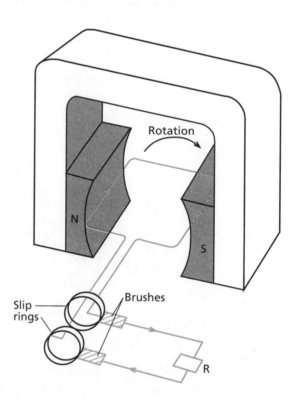

Fig. 22.2 Simple a.c. dynamo

The outputs of both a simple a.c. and a simple d.c. dynamo are shown in Figs. 22.3 (a) and (b), respectively. In each case the coil starts from the vertical.

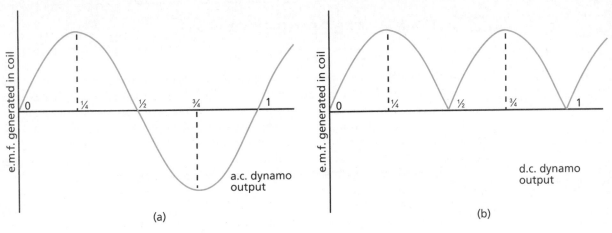

(a)

(b)

Fig. 22.3

22.4 The transformer

A transformer is illustrated diagrammatically in Fig. 22.4. The two coils shown are wound on a laminated soft–iron core. When an alternating current passes through the primary an alternating magnetic field is set up in the core. Since the flux through the secondary coil is changing, this induces an e.m.f. in it which is also alternating. The size of this induced e.m.f. will depend on the e.m.f. applied to the primary and on the relative numbers of turns in the two coils:

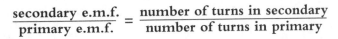

$$\frac{\text{secondary e.m.f.}}{\text{primary e.m.f.}} = \frac{\text{number of turns in secondary}}{\text{number of turns in primary}}$$

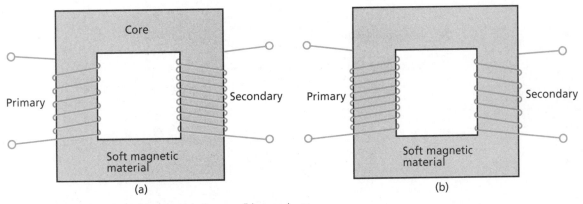

Fig. 22.4 Transformers: (a) step-up; (b) step-down

If the ratio of the number of turns is greater than one, the secondary e.m.f. will be greater than the primary and we have a *step-up* transformer. A ratio less than unity gives a *step-down* transformer.

A transformer is designed to minimize energy losses. The windings are composed of low–resistance copper coils to reduce the heating losses. The core is laminated, that is it is constructed of layers of magnetic material fixed together and insulated from each other by varnish or oxide coatings. This ensures that, although e.m.f.'s are induced in the core, as well as the secondary coil by the changing magnetic field, currents cannot flow between the laminated layers. Thus the total current in the transformer core is kept to as small a value as possible, as are the energy losses due to its heating effect.

Efficient core design also means that all the magnetic flux produced by the primary passes through the secondary. In practice this is best achieved by winding the primary and secondary on top of one another. In a good transformer energy losses are small and we may assume that:

secondary power output = primary power input

22.5 Power transmission

One of the main advantages of alternating current is that it can easily be changed from one voltage to another by a transformer, with little loss of energy. For this reason, electric power is generally conveyed by alternating current, as it can be transformed to a very high voltage and transmitted over large distances, with small power losses as explained below. This has two advantages. Firstly, electricity can be generated where water power, coal and oil are easily obtainable or at conveniently sited nuclear power stations, and conveyed to all parts of the country by high voltage overhead power lines. Secondly, power is easily made available wherever the peak demand occurs. For example, during the day power which has been generated in an area that has little industry may be used in a more industrialized area that has at this time a greater demand.

In Great Britain electricity is generated at 11 000 V and then stepped up to as much as 400 000 V by transformers. It is subsequently stepped down in stages at substations in the neighbourhood where the energy is to be consumed. The reason electrical energy is transmitted at such high voltages can clearly be seen from the following calculation.

Find the power wasted as heat in the cables when 10 kW is transmitted through a cable of resistance 0.5 Ω at (a) 200 V; (b) 200 000 V.

(a) The current is given by the equation:

$$\text{current} = \frac{\text{power}}{\text{voltage}} = \frac{10\ 000}{200}$$

$$= 50 \text{ A}$$

Therefore the power lost in the cable $= I^2R$

$$= 50^2 \times 0.5 \text{ W}$$

$$= 1250 \text{ W}$$

(b)   The current $= \dfrac{\text{power}}{\text{voltage}} = \dfrac{10\ 000}{2000\ 000} = 0.05 \text{ A}$

Therefore the power lost in the cable $= I^2R$

$$= 0.05^2 \times 0.5 \text{ W}$$

$$= 0.00125 \text{ W}$$

At 200 V more than 10% of the energy transmitted is wasted in heating the cable. At 200 000 V this energy loss is reduced by a factor of a million and is negligible.

Summary

1   Whenever a conductor moves relative to a magnetic field an electromotive force (e.m.f.) is induced in the conductor. The strength of the e.m.f. is proportional to the strength of the magnetic field and the speed of the relative motion.

2   The effect outlined in point 1 is the basis of a dynamo.

3   A transformer changes the value of an alternating e.m.f. either up or down.

4   For a transformer

$$\frac{\textbf{secondary e.m.f.}}{\textbf{primary e.m.f.}} = \frac{\textbf{number of turns in secondary}}{\textbf{number of turns in primary}}$$

5   Power is transmitted over long distances at high voltage and low current. This reduces energy losses in the transmission cables.

Chapter 23
Electron beams

23.1 Thermionic emission

Metals contain many electrons which are loosely attached to their atoms. If a wire is heated to a high temperature the extra energy given to the electrons enables them to break away from the metal structure and exist outside as an electron cloud. This is called **thermionic emission**.

Strontium and barium are good electron emitters but are not suitable to be made into a thin wire. Tungsten, however, can be made into a very thin wire and can withstand high temperatures without melting. Thus tungsten is used as the base of the wire and its surface coated with barium or strontium which emit well at these temperatures. The wire is heated electrically, usually by using a 6.3 V supply which can be obtained from either a d.c. or an a.c. source.

23.2 The diode

The electrons released from a wire by thermionic emission form a cloud around it which prevents further emission. This cloud may be removed by placing a plate near to the wire and connecting a steady voltage between them, so that the plate (anode) is more positive than the wire (cathode). It is necessary to place this whole arrangement in an evacuated tube so that the passage of the electrons is not inhibited by the presence of air molecules. This arrangement is known as a **diode**.

The characteristic action of a diode may be investigated using the circuit shown in Fig. 23.1(a). The voltage applied to the diode is varied using the source B, and the resulting current is registered on the milliammeter. Figure 23.1(b) shows a typical set of results.

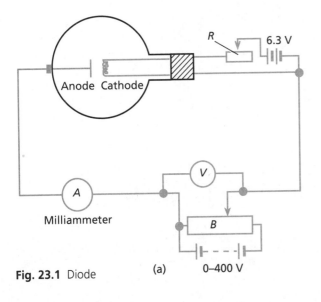

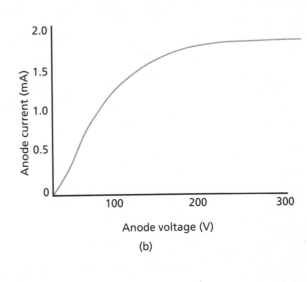

Fig. 23.1 Diode

The actual values of the voltage applied and the current obtained will depend on the actual diode used. However, the general shape of the graph will be similar in all cases. When no voltage is applied between the anode and cathode the electrons released by thermionic emission remain near the cathode. If a small positive potential difference is applied between the anode and cathode, some of the electrons in the cloud move across the empty space to the anode. Here they flow through the anode circuit back to the cathode, and a small current is registered.

The electrons crossing to the anode create a negative charge in the space between anode and cathode. This negative space charge repels some electrons back to the cathode. Thus not all the electrons emitted from the cathode reach the anode when the potential difference is small. However, as the potential difference increases, a larger proportion of the electrons emitted do reach the anode. At large voltages all the electrons emitted per second reach the anode and increasing the voltage further will not increase the current. The maximum current is known as the *saturation current*.

No current flows when the anode potential is negative with respect to the cathode. All the electrons emitted are repelled back to the cathode. The diode will thus only allow current to flow in one direction; for this reason it is known as a **valve**.

Suppose an alternating voltage is connected to a diode valve with a resistance R of a few thousand ohms in series with it (Fig. 23.2(a)). The diode will only pass current during the positive half of each cycle. An oscilloscope connected across the resistance R will show a voltage of the form illustrated in Fig. 23.2(b). The applied voltage has been rectified (converted from a.c. to d.c.) by the diode valve which has been used as a 'rectifier'.

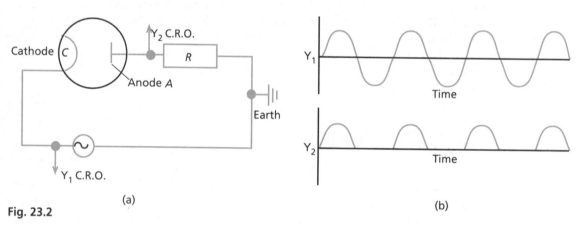

Fig. 23.2

One diode only allows half of an alternating current to flow through a load R; the other half is cut out. A more even supply of power can be obtained using the circuit in Fig. 23.3(a). This makes the whole of the alternating current flow one way through R. When terminal 1 is positive, current flows through diode A, the resistor R and diode C and returns to terminal 2. When terminal 2 is positive, current flows through diode B, the resistor R and diode D before returning to terminal 1. The output waveform is shown under the circuit diagram.

A smoother output may be obtained by using the circuit shown in Fig. 23.3(b). This is the same as that shown in Fig. 23.3(a) with the addition of a smoothing capacitor C in parallel with the resistor R. While the potential difference across R and C is rising to its peak value, the capacitor C is charged up. Then while the output of the rectifier drops rapidly to zero, the capacitor supplies charge, causing the current through R to fall more slowly. The larger the value of the capacitor, the smoother is the final output. The output waveform is shown under the circuit diagram in Fig. 23.3(b).

23.3 Cathode rays (electron beams)

Since electrons are easily produced by thermionic emission, experiments on electrons can be conveniently carried out using this source.

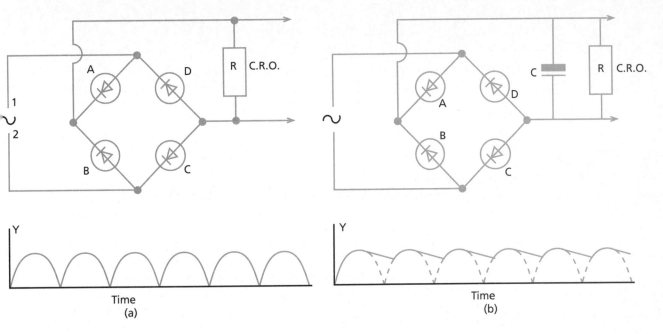

C.R.O.

Fig. 23.3

In the Maltese cross tube illustrated in Fig. 23.4 the anode *A* is cylindrical and is maintained at a positive potential of a few thousand volts relative to the cathode *C*. This part of the apparatus is called an *electron gun*. The electrons are accelerated in the space between the cathode and anode and pass through the cylindrical anode. The Maltese cross shown is at right angles to the beam of cathode rays and is connected to the anode. The cross is thus at the same potential as the anode and the electrons move between the two at a constant speed (that is, they are not accelerated). When the electrons strike the screen some of their kinetic energy is converted into light, thus showing the position of the beam. A sharp shadow of the cross is seen on the screen, suggesting that the electrons emitted from the cathode travel in straight lines along the tube.

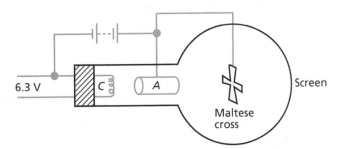

Fig. 23.4
Maltese-cross
tube

23.4 The effect of electric and magnetic fields

The deflection tube illustrated in Fig. 23.5 is similar to the Maltese cross tube, except that it contains two horizontal plates *P* and *Q* instead of the cross. The electrons emitted from the cathode are accelerated in the same way. They then pass between *P* and *Q* before striking the centre of the screen. However, if a large potential difference is connected between *P* and *Q*, the electron beam will be deflected. If, for example, *P* is positive relative to *Q* the electrons will be attracted to it and the beam will be deflected towards it. The beam is deflected downwards if *Q* is the more positive plate. The amount of deflection depends on the potential difference.

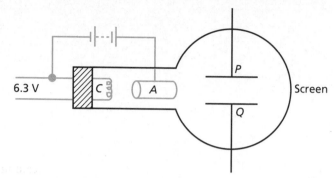

Fig. 23.5
Deflection tube

If two bar magnets are placed, one each side of the tube, with opposite poles facing, the beam will be deflected. This is the same effect as that responsible for the force on a current-carrying wire placed in a magnetic field and thus for the rotation of an electric motor. In place of the bar magnets, the magnetic field may be produced by using two vertical coils, one each side of the tube. If a current of between one and two amps is passed through these coils connected in series, a magnetic field results in the space between them. It has already been seen, in Unit 21.4, that a beam of charged particles passing through a magnetic field will experience a force at right angles to the field and their direction of travel. In the deflection tube the force acting on the electrons is initially either up or down, but, as the beam is deflected by this force, the force remains at right angles to the beam. The amount of deflection in a magnetic field depends on the strength of the field; in the case of the coils this depends on the current passing through them.

There is one further common type of deflection tube, known as the fine beam tube (Fig. 21.9). It contains a conical metal anode A, with a hole at the top over the cathode C. When a potential difference of a few thousand volts is connected between the two an electron beam is emitted vertically. The tube has a very small amount of hydrogen in it. The fast-moving electrons produce a fine beam of light as they ionize the hydrogen molecules. The beam shows the path of the electrons. The electrons may be deflected by connecting a potential difference between the two plates D_1 and D_2 just above the anode, or by passing an electric current through the two large coils placed one each side of the tube. In the latter case the beam of electrons may be deflected into a closed circle as the force is always at right angles to the direction of travel of the electrons.

23.5 Cathode ray oscilloscope

The cathode ray tube shown in Fig. 23.6 is very similar to the deflection tube illustrated in Fig. 23.5. It relies on exactly the same principle for its operation but has an additional pair of plates X_1 and X_2 so that the electron beam may be deflected horizontally as well as vertically.

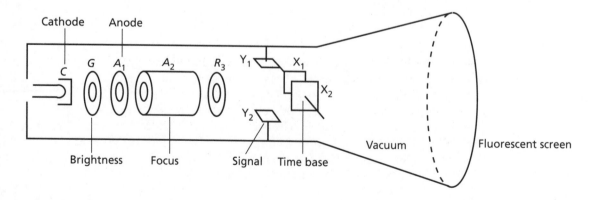

Fig. 23.6 Cathode ray oscilloscope

The cathode C emits electrons which are accelerated to the anode A by a high positive potential difference. In practice the anode usually consists of more than one plate or cylinder (A_1, A_2) so that it behaves like an electron lens and is able to focus the beam. The plate G is slightly negative compared to the anode. The number of electrons reaching the screen is controlled by how negative G is.

The cathode ray oscilloscope is excellent for use as a voltmeter. As no charge passes between the plates, when the beam is deflected, the tube draws no current from the component whose voltage it is recording; that is, it has an extremely high resistance.

If a d.c. voltage is to be measured it is connected between the plates Y_1 and Y_2. The spot on the screen will move a certain distance vertically which should be measured. If the oscilloscope has a calibrated scale this reading may immediately be converted to volts. If it is not calibrated a battery of known voltage should be connected to the oscilloscope and the deflection it causes recorded.

If it is required to measure an a.c. voltage, this should be connected to the plates Y_1 and Y_2. The length of the vertical line which results gives the value of the peak to peak voltage. However, if it is desired to see how the value of the voltage changes with time, the time base facility should be used. This provides a changing voltage connected to the X-plates, thus deflecting the beam horizontally. The spot thus repeatedly moves across the screen at a speed dictated by a switch controlling the time base frequency. Thus, as the spot moves up and down in response to the a.c. voltage connected to the Y-plates, it moves horizontally at a steady speed. A graph (Fig. 23.2(b) Y_1) is obtained with voltage as the Y-axis and time as the X-axis.

The cathode ray oscilloscope may be used to display any a.c. voltage; for example that across a resistor or that given by a microphone when sound falls on its diaphragm. It may also be used to examine the small voltage associated with the human heartbeat. The time base mechanism makes the oscilloscope suitable for use as a timing device. A pulse can be displayed on the screen at the instant it is emitted by a radar system and again when it is received back after reflection by an object in the Earth's atmosphere or in the space beyond. The distance between the two pulses on the screen gives the time taken for the return journey of the pulse. As the velocity of radio waves is known to be 3×10^8 m/s, the distance between the emitter and the reflecting object can be calculated.

The cathode ray tube is the basis of a television set. The time base causes the spot to cross the screen many times in quick succession, each time a little below the last, so that the whole screen is covered. In Great Britain and many other countries 625 lines are drawn on the screen in 1/25 second in this way. As the spot moves across the screen its intensity is varied by the incoming signal, thus causing a picture to be 'painted' on the screen. The whole process is then repeated. Thus 25 slightly different pictures appear on the screen every second, giving the impression of continuous movement.

23.6 Semiconductor materials

Materials which allow electrons to flow through them are called conductors. Metals are the best conductors. The outermost electrons in each atom are so loosely attached that they are able to move freely between atoms. They are called 'free electrons'.

Materials which do not conduct charge are called insulators. All their electrons are tightly held to atoms and are not normally free to move. Glass, rubber, polythene and plastics are good examples of insulators.

A few materials are neither good conductors nor good insulators, but have conducting properties between the two groups. These materials, which are known as semiconductors, contain a small number of free and mobile charges. The best known semiconductor material is silicon although there are others, such as germanium, lead sulphide and gallium arsenide.

In a pure semiconductor such as silicon, all the outer electrons of the atoms form bonds with neighbouring atoms and there are virtually no 'free electrons' left over for conduction. However, as the temperature is increased, the thermal energies of the vibrating atoms in the crystal cause some electrons to break free. More thermal electrons are freed as the temperature rises. Every electron that becomes free leaves a gap or hole in an atom. Since the atoms are normally neutral the hole behaves as if it has a positive charge. Like electrons these positive holes seem to move through the semiconductor material and form part of the electric current in it. Conduction in a semiconductor by means of thermal electrons and positive holes is called intrinsic conduction.

A thermistor is a piece of semiconductor material behaving in this way. When cold the thermistor has a high resistance. As its temperature increases more electrons and holes are released, improving the intrinsic conduction of the material and hence lowering its resistance. Thermistors are used to prevent large currents flowing through lamp filaments and electric motors at the moment of switching on. They can also be used to operate thermostats and fire alarms.

Cadmium sulphide is one of several semiconductor materials whose resistance varies with the amount of light falling on it. As light energy is absorbed, electrons and holes are released and become available for conduction. The brighter the light the more of these charge carriers are released and the further the resistance of the material falls. Such semiconductor materials are used in light-dependent resistors (LDR).

Small quantities of different elements can be added to a semiconductor material which greatly change its conduction properties. Conduction caused by these impurities is called extrinsic conduction or impurity conduction. Adding such impurities to semiconductor materials is called doping. Silicon atoms have four electrons in their outer shells and all are required for bonding with its four nearest neighbours. If some atoms with five electrons in their outer shells are added to the silicon crystal, they provide one spare electron each. Phosphorus, antimony and arsenic are used to dope silicon in this way and provide spare electrons for conduction. Such doped material is called n-type silicon as it has an excess of negative charge carriers.

If materials such as aluminium, gallium and indium, with three electrons in the outer shells of their atoms, are used to dope the crystal, it will have one electron missing in its structure for each impurity atom present. Semiconductor material with extra positive hole charge carriers (missing electrons) is called p-type material.

23.7 The p–n junction diode

Such a diode consists of a single crystal of silicon or germanium, part of which has been doped so that it contains an excess of positive charges (p-type). The rest of the crystal has had a different impurity added so that it contains an excess of electrons (n-type). It is the existence of the junction between the two types of material which enables the device to act as a rectifier. It is therefore called a p–n junction diode.

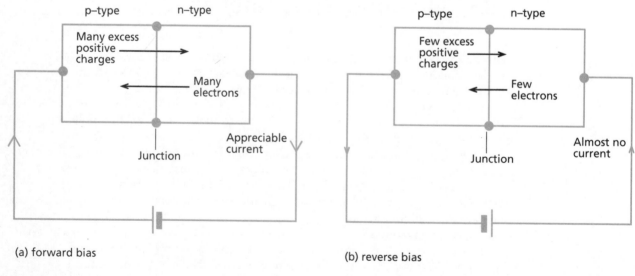

(a) forward bias   (b) reverse bias

Fig. 23.7

Suppose that a battery is connected across a junction diode as in Fig. 23.7(a), the so-called forward bias connection. The battery urges the excess positive charges and the electrons to cross the junction and so constitute a current. When the battery is reversed the excess charges are discouraged from crossing the junction and no current flows (Fig. 23.7(b)). This one-way conduction property of a junction diode may be used to convert alternating current to direct current in the way described for the thermionic diode in Unit 23.2.

23.8 The light emitting diode (LED)

Junction diodes made of gallium arsenide and gallium phosphide emit light when a forward biased current flows through them. The colour of the light depends on the semiconductor material. The main advantage of the light emitting diode, compared to the filament lamp, is the low current and hence the low heat production. To limit the current to a low and safe value for the LED a protective resistor is connected in series with the diode (Fig. 23.8).

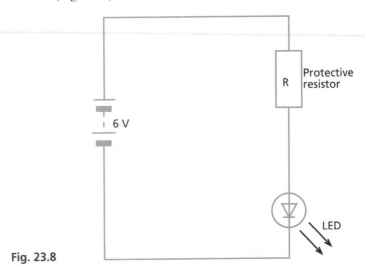

Fig. 23.8

23.9 The transistor

The transistor is a semiconductor sandwich usually made of silicon. A thin layer of p–type silicon sandwiched between two layers of n-type silicon forms an npn transistor. A pnp transistor has the types of silicon reversed.

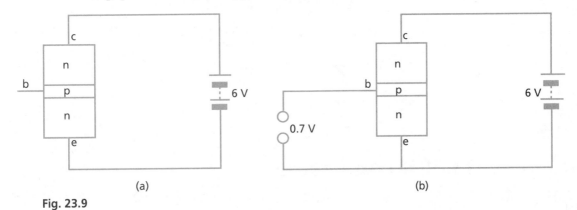

(a)   (b)

Fig. 23.9

Consider an npn transistor, shown diagrammatically in Fig. 23.9. The n-type regions are the emitter and collector; the thin p-type region is the base. If a potential difference is applied between the emitter and collector as shown in Fig. 23.9(a), the upper junction is reverse biased and no current flows through the transistor. If the lower junction is now forward biased by applying a small potential difference across it, as in Fig. 23.9(b), electrons flow from the emitter into the base. The base is so thin that most of these electrons drift across into the collector; the top junction is conducting and a current flows through the transistor as a result. A small current in the base or input circuit enables a much larger current to flow round the collector or output circuit. These results mean that:

① The transistor can be used as a switch, because no current flows in the collector circuit unless a current flows in the base circuit.

② The transistor can be used to amplify current changes as a small change in the base current produces a large change in the collector current.

In Fig. 23.9(b) note that the base and collector circuits share a common connection at the emitter. Used in this way the transistor is said to be in the common–emitter mode.

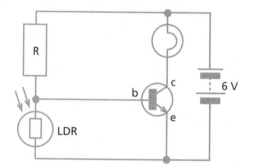

Fig. 23.10

    Figure 23.10 shows an npn transistor being used as a light operated transistor switch. When light falls on the LDR its resistance is low, the input voltage to the base is below about 0.7 V and the transistor is switched off. No current flows in the collector circuit and the lamp is off. When the LDR is shielded from the light its resistance rises. The input voltage to the base also rises above about 0.7 V causing current to flow in the base circuit. A larger current flows in the collector circuit and the lamp comes on. The value of the resistor R is determined by the type of transistor and LDR used.

    Figure 23.11 shows the transistor being used as a current amplifier. Small variations in the base current, caused by the microphone, lead to much greater variations in the collector current. The current amplification or gain of a transistor is given by the formula:

$$\text{current gain} = \frac{\text{collector current}}{\text{base current}}$$

The value of the current gain of a transistor can be anywhere between 10 and 1000 with a typical value of about 100.

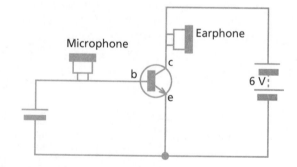

Fig. 23.11

23.10 The bistable

A bistable contains two transistors (Fig. 23.12). If lamp L_1 comes on when the circuit is first connected then transistor T_1 is 'on' and T_2 is 'off'. The circuit stays in this state, i.e. it is latched on. If switch S_1 is momentarily closed, the base of T_1 is connected to 0 V, i.e. it is no longer forward biased and switches 'off'. L_1 therefore goes off and L_2 lights up because T_2 comes on as its base is now connected to 6 V via R_1 and L_1, i.e. it is forward biased. The circuit will stay in this second stable state (bistable) until S_2 is closed momentarily, when L_1 lights again. A second type of bistable, made from two NOR gates, is described in Unit 23.12.

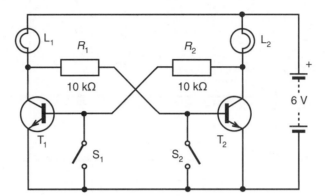

Fig. 23.12

23.11 Electronic systems

Electronics systems are becoming increasingly more common and more important as time goes on. These systems can be described and understood in terms of building blocks and block diagrams. They handle and process two different kinds of information: analogue and digital. Here we confine our attention to digital systems.

In a digital system all information is processed in the form of digits; for example 1995 has four digits and each digit tells us how many thousands, hundreds, tens and ones of years there are. Calculators and computers represent numbers by binary digits. There are only two digits, 0 and 1, in binary arithmetic, rather than the ten digits 0 to 9 that we are used to in our usual arithmetic. For example the number 6 becomes 110 when expressed in binary digits. 110 stands for 1 'four', 1 'two' and 0 'ones'. Each of the binary digits 110 is called a bit and an electronic system which handles information in this way is a binary digital system. Note that calculators and computers convert the binary numbers into normal arithmetic before displaying the answer.

23.12 Logic gates

The use of a transistor as a switch has already been described. A variety of switches or building blocks called logic gates are used in digital systems. These blocks are like 'gates' because they have to be opened to let information pass through to reach their outputs. Each type of gate is opened by a particular combination of information fed to its inputs in binary code.

There are five basic types of logic gate from which all the more complicated ones are constructed. They are shown in Fig. 23.13. A truth table is a very simple way of describing all the possible combinations of inputs and outputs produced by a particular gate, or collection of gates. The name of a particular gate describes how it makes its decisions. It tells us which combination of high or NOT high (low) inputs produces a high output signal. Logic 0 represents a low input or output and logic 1 a high one. For example an AND gate only gives a high output (1) when both inputs are high (1).

Type	Symbol	Same as	Truth table	Output is high (1) when:
NOT	A ⊳o— Y	INVERTER	<table><tr><td>Input A</td><td>Output Y</td></tr><tr><td>0</td><td>1</td></tr><tr><td>1</td><td>0</td></tr></table>	Input A is NOT high
OR	A, B ⊃— Y		<table><tr><td>A</td><td>B</td><td>Y</td></tr><tr><td>0</td><td>0</td><td>0</td></tr><tr><td>1</td><td>0</td><td>1</td></tr><tr><td>0</td><td>1</td><td>1</td></tr><tr><td>1</td><td>1</td><td>1</td></tr></table>	Input A OR B is high
NOR	A, B ⊃o— Y	OR–NOT	<table><tr><td>A</td><td>B</td><td>Y</td></tr><tr><td>0</td><td>0</td><td>1</td></tr><tr><td>1</td><td>0</td><td>0</td></tr><tr><td>0</td><td>1</td><td>0</td></tr><tr><td>1</td><td>1</td><td>0</td></tr></table>	Neither input A NOR input B is high
AND	A, B ⊐— Y		<table><tr><td>A</td><td>B</td><td>Y</td></tr><tr><td>0</td><td>0</td><td>0</td></tr><tr><td>1</td><td>0</td><td>0</td></tr><tr><td>0</td><td>1</td><td>0</td></tr><tr><td>1</td><td>1</td><td>1</td></tr></table>	Input A AND input B are high
NAND	A, B ⊐o— Y	AND–NOT	<table><tr><td>A</td><td>B</td><td>Y</td></tr><tr><td>0</td><td>0</td><td>1</td></tr><tr><td>1</td><td>0</td><td>1</td></tr><tr><td>0</td><td>1</td><td>1</td></tr><tr><td>1</td><td>1</td><td>0</td></tr></table>	Input A AND input B are NOT both high

Fig. 23.13

Now, rather than manufacturing separate circuits containing individual transistors, integrated circuits (ICs) are used. Each integrated circuit consists of a very small single chip of silicon on which groups of components, including several transistors, are manufactured.

Each gate is referred to as a **processor**. Each of its **inputs** may be connected to a switch or to a sensor such as a light-dependent resistor or a thermistor. The **output** is connected to a buzzer, lamp, LED or relay.

Two NOR gates may be used to make a bistable. The diagrams in Fig. 23.14 show how it works. The output of a NOR gate is 1 only when both inputs are zero.

In (a) the bistable is set with S = 1 and C = 0. Since S = 1, $\bar{Q}$ = 0. As both inputs to the lower NOR gate are at 0, Q = 1. In (b), S has changed to 0. This does not affect $\bar{Q}$ or Q, so Q = 1 still.

However, in (c) S = 0 and C = 1. This means that $\bar{Q}$ = 1 and Q = 0. In (d) C goes back to 0. This does not affect $\bar{Q}$ or Q.

The bistable remembers which of S or C was last in the logic state 1. The output Q of the bistable has two states, either 0 or 1. The bistable is the basis of the binary counting system.

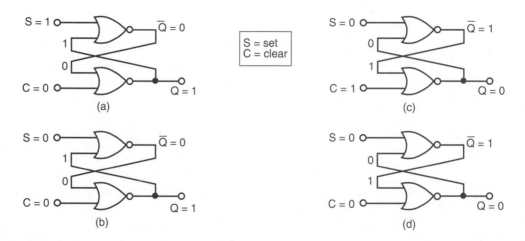

Fig. 23.14

Summary

1   When a wire is heated electrons are released from the surface.

2   A thermionic diode contains a wire which is heated electrically (the cathode) and a metal plate (or cylinder) called the anode which is positive with respect to the cathode. Electrons released by the cathode are accelerated to the anode. Electrons cannot be made to flow in the opposite direction.

3   The diode (or electron gun) is the source of the electron beam in a Maltese cross tube, a deflection tube and a cathode ray oscilloscope.

4   Materials, such as metals, which readily allow electrons to flow through them are called conductors. Materials which do not are called insulators. A few materials, such as silicon and germanium, have conducting properties between the two groups and are called semiconductors.

5   Some materials, cadmium sulphide, for example, have less resistance when light falls on them. Such materials are used in light dependent resistors (LDR).

6   A diode can be made from, for example, a single crystal of germanium which has been doped. Such a diode (junction diode) behaves in a circuit in a similar way to a thermionic diode.

7   Junction diodes made of gallium arsenide or phosphide emit light when a forward biased current flows through them. They are called light emitting diodes (LED).

8   A transistor is a semiconductor sandwich usually made from silicon. A thin layer of p-type silicon sandwiched between two layers of n-type silicon forms an npn transistor. A pnp transistor has the types of silicon reversed.

9   A transistor is often used as a switch or to amplify a current.

10   Digital electronic systems use binary arithmetic and are the basis of calculators and computers.

11   There are many types of logic gate. Each type of gate is 'opened' by a particular combination of information fed to its inputs in binary code.

Chapter 24
Radioactivity and atomic structure

It has already been seen that electrons passing through a gas ionize the molecules of the gas (for example in the fine beam tube – Unit 23.4). Due to the electrical forces of attraction and repulsion, any charged particle passing near to a molecule will tend to ionize it – that is, split it into positively and negatively charged parts. This property of charged particles may be used to detect their presence.

24.1 Radiation detectors

One of the most widely used detectors is the Geiger–Müller (GM) tube shown in Fig. 24.1.

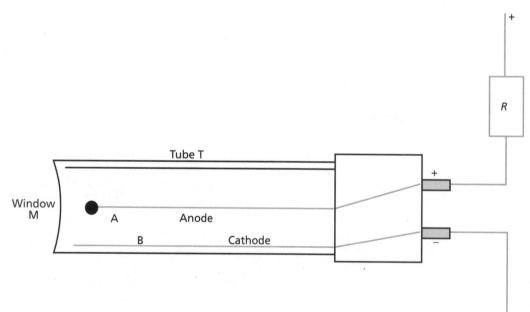

Fig. 24.1 Geiger tube

It consists of a small closed tube T, with a thin mica end window M, and contains a gas such as argon at about half atmospheric pressure. A thin wire A, which acts as the anode, passes down the centre of the tube and is insulated from it. The inside of the tube is coated with a conductor and forms the second electrode B. A potential difference of about 450 V is applied between the electrodes.

When a charged particle enters the tube through the thin mica window some argon atoms are ionized. Many more atoms throughout the tube then become ionized. The negative ions produced are attracted towards the central wire A, the positive ions going towards *B*. A current is thus obtained in the circuit for a short time. It is called a pulse of current and causes a voltage pulse in the high resistance *R*. The 450 V power supply and the resistance *R* are contained in an electronic unit such as a scaler, which counts individual pulses, or a ratemeter, which gives the average count rate.

The presence of X-rays and γ-rays may also be detected using a GM tube.

24.2 Atomic structure

Atoms may be regarded as being like miniature solar systems. An atom is thought to have a central nucleus, consisting of tightly packed particles called protons and neutrons, with electrons revolving round it. Evidence for this model comes from a series of experiments carried out by Geiger and Marsden at Manchester University in 1911. Alpha particles emitted from a radioactive source were scattered by a thin foil of gold. A very small fraction of the particles were scattered through very large angles (some through more than 90°) and Rutherford suggested that these had come very close to a high concentration of positive charge (an atomic nucleus) and had been deflected by the large electrical force of repulsion.

In the nucleus of an atom each proton has a positive charge equal in magnitude to the charge on an electron, and the number of protons in the nucleus of an atom is equal to the number of electrons in the atom. The atom is therefore electrically neutral. The chemical properties of an atom and hence the element to which it belongs are dictated by the number and arrangement of electrons in it, and this in turn depends on the number of protons in the nucleus, known as the **atomic number**, denoted by *Z*.

Neutrons are similar in mass to protons, both being nearly 2000 times as massive as electrons. The mass of an atom is thus almost entirely due to the masses of the protons and neutrons contained in its nucleus. The total number of protons and neutrons in the nucleus of an atom is known as the atom's **mass number**, denoted by *A*. Thus if the number of neutrons is denoted by *N* we have

$$A = Z + N$$

It is possible for one or more of the peripheral electrons of an atom to become detached, thus leaving the atom with a net positive charge. It is then known as a positive ion. It is also possible for an atom to gain one or more electrons, becoming a negative ion. It is only in radioactive disintegrations that the number of protons or neutrons in an atom changes. All the electrical and chemical properties of an atom are explained in terms of the transfer of electrons.

Helium has a nucleus containing two protons and two neutrons, and two peripheral electrons. When an atom disintegrates by means of **alpha particle decay** (see Unit 24.4) it loses two protons and becomes an atom of the element two below it in the periodic table of elements. As it has also lost two neutrons, its mass number has fallen by four.

Beta decay seems to take place by a neutron changing to a proton, which remains in the nucleus, and an electron, which is emitted. The atom concerned has gained a proton and thus becomes an atom of the element one up in the periodic table. Its mass number has not changed.

24.3 Isotopes

From the previous discussion it can be seen that two atoms of an element may exist (that is the atoms have the same number of protons) which have different numbers of neutrons and hence different mass numbers. These atoms are said to be **isotopes of the same element**.

At the lower end of the periodic table the number of neutrons present in an atom is equal to, or nearly equal to, the number of protons. Elements of high mass number consist of atoms with very many more neutrons than protons. It is these atoms which are more likely to disintegrate. It seems that a large number of excess neutrons in an atom leads to instability and the likelihood of spontaneous disintegration. Generally speaking it is the elements of high mass number which exhibit this property of radioactivity.

24.4 Radioactivity

A number of naturally occurring substances emit particles or radiations which ionize gases. Marie Curie and her husband did much of the early work on radioactive substances and showed that amongst the most active were those containing uranium, polonium and radium.

By 1899 Rutherford had shown that the particles or radiations emitted by radioactive substances fell into three categories which he called **alpha (α), beta (β)** and **gamma (γ) rays**.

Alpha rays are helium ions – that is, helium atoms which have lost two electrons, and hence have a positive charge. From a particular radioactive substance they are all ejected with approximately the same velocity and hence kinetic energy. They have a range of a few centimetres in air at atmospheric pressure, but most are stopped by a thick sheet of paper. Like all charged particles they lose their energy by continuous ionization and the fact that they produce many ions per centimetre of path means that they travel relatively short distances. Being charged particles they are deflected by both electric and magnetic fields.

Beta rays are streams of high energy electrons similar to cathode rays but travelling much faster. They are emitted with velocities approaching that of light (3×10^8 m/s) and, as they do not form such a high density of ions along their track, their range is greater than that of alpha rays. Beta rays are negatively charged and are thus deflected in the opposite direction to alpha particles in both electric and magnetic fields.

Gamma rays are very short wavelength radiations similar to X-rays, which can penetrate several centimetres of dense metal such as lead. They do not produce continuous ionization but lose their energy in one interaction with a molecule. The fact that they cannot be deflected by electric or magnetic fields indicates that they are not charged particles.

An idea of the range of alpha, beta and gamma rays may be obtained by placing sources emitting these separate rays in front of a GM tube connected to a scaler. The number of counts recorded by the scaler in a given time is noted with different absorbers (sheets of paper, aluminium or lead of different thicknesses) between the source and the tube. Alphas are stopped by a thin sheet of paper. It is found that gamma rays in particular and beta rays to a lesser extent are very difficult to stop or screen, and thus may present a safety hazard. Gamma ray sources are kept in lead containers, the walls of which are often several centimetres thick.

If the GM tube and scaler are switched on in the absence of a source and the absorbers, some counts will be recorded. This count rate, which is slow, is due to radiation which is always present in the atmosphere. It is called background radiation, and should be subtracted from the counts recorded when a source is present, to give the true count rate due to the source.

24.5 Uses of radioactivity

Radioactive materials have many uses in medicine, industry and agriculture.

In **medicine** iodine 131 is used to see if the thyroid gland is working properly. The thyroid gland absorbs iodine, so a dose of radioactive iodine (tracer) is given to a patient.

Doctors then measure the radioactivity of the patient's throat, to see how well his thyroid is working. The tracer has a short half-life.

Cobalt 60 emits high-energy gamma rays and is used in the treatment of cancer. A strong beam of this radiation is directed onto the cancerous tissue to kill the cancer cells. The treatment has unpleasant side-effects but is often successful in slowing down the growth of, or even completely curing, the cancer.

Cobalt 60 is also used to sterilize medical equipment such as syringes, dressings and surgeons' instruments. These items are first packed into sealed plastic bags and then irradiated with gamma rays which kill any bacteria on them.

In **industry** radioactive tracers may be used to detect leaks in underground pipes. The tracer is fed into the pipe and then a Geiger tube is used above ground to detect any increase in the radiation level and hence the leak. This method is cheaper and quicker than digging up the entire length of the pipe.

A beta particle source may be used to automatically control the thickness of sheets of paper, plastic and metal being rolled in a mill. The source is placed on one side of the sheet and a Geiger tube on the other. If the count rate falls this means the sheet coming from the rollers is too thick and the rollers are automatically moved a little closer together by electronic means. The source should have a long half-life.

A radioisotope of iron is used in industry to estimate the wear on moving parts of machinery. For example, a piston ring made of radioactive iron is put into an engine and run for several days. At the end the oil from the engine is collected and, from the amount of radioactivity present, engineers can estimate the amount of wear of the ring.

An alpha particle source is used in some smoke detectors. The smoke prevents the alpha particles reaching the detector and this sets off the alarm.

Tracers are used in **agriculture**. Radioactive phosphorus is used as a tracer to show how well plants are absorbing phosphorus.

Sometimes gamma radiation is used to prolong the shelf-life of pre-packaged foods. Gamma rays kill the bacteria in the food and so eliminate the risk of food poisoning. As the gamma rays also kill some cells in the food itself such treatment can alter the taste of the food.

24.6 Radioactive decay

By 1903 Rutherford had come to the conclusion that radioactivity is the result of the spontaneous disintegration of an atom during which it emits an alpha or beta ray. Simultaneously the atom changes into one of another element which may itself be radioactive. The following are examples of such disintegrations.

$$^{238}_{92}U \rightarrow \ ^{4}_{2}He + \ ^{234}_{90}Th \qquad \alpha\text{-decay}$$

$$^{234}_{90}Th \rightarrow \ ^{0}_{-1}e + \ ^{234}_{91}Pa \qquad \beta\text{-decay}$$

$$^{234}_{91}Pa \rightarrow \ ^{0}_{-1}e + \ ^{234}_{92}U \qquad \beta\text{-decay}$$

The numbers above the symbols are the mass numbers of the atoms; those below are the atomic numbers.

It is impossible to predict which particular atom in a sample will change in this way; that is, the disintegration of an atom is a random event. However, in a sample containing a large number of atoms, the number which disintegrate each second will depend on the number of undecayed atoms left. Thus if the number of disintegrations per second is recorded (by counting the number of particles emitted) and plotted against time an exponential graph results (Fig. 24.2).

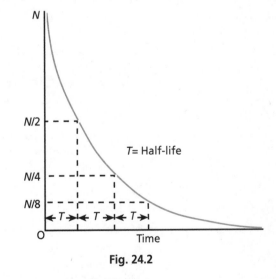

Fig. 24.2

As can be seen from this graph, an infinite time is taken for all the atoms of a sample to disintegrate. It is therefore meaningless to talk about the 'life' of a sample. However, **the time taken for half the undecayed atoms in any given sample of the substance to disintegrate is finite, and the same whatever the number of undecayed atoms present initially**. This time T is known as the **half-life** of the substance. It is different for different radioactive materials.

24.7 Safety

Exposure of the body to radiation from atomic disintegrations can have undesirable effects of a long- or short-term nature. The precise result of exposure depends on the nature of the radiation, the part of the body irradiated and the dose received. The hazard from alpha particles is slight, unless the source enters the body, since they cannot penetrate the outer layers of skin. Beta particles are more penetrating, although most of their energy is absorbed by surface tissues. Gamma rays present the main external radiation hazard since they penetrate deeply into the body.

Radiation can cause immediate damage to cells, and is accompanied by radiation burns (redness of skin followed by blistering and sores, the severity of these depending on the dose received), radiation sickness and possibly death. Effects such as cancer and leukaemia may appear many years later, due to the uncontrolled multiplication of some cells set off by exposure to radiation. Hereditary effects may also occur in succeeding generations due to genetic changes. The most susceptible parts of the body are the reproductive organs and blood-forming organs such as the liver.

Because of the hazards it is essential that the correct procedure be adopted when using radioactive substances. Briefly it is as follows:

1. Sources should only be held with forceps, never with the hand. This avoids any possibility of some of the substance transferring to the surface of the skin or lodging under a nail.

2. Any cuts on the hand should be covered before using sources.

3. Sources should not be pointed towards the human body.

4. Sources should be returned to their container as soon as they are no longer needed for an experiment. If possible, permanent storage should be within two containers.

5. A check should be made at the end of an experiment to see that all sources are present in their allotted containers.

6. Mouth pipettes should never be used with liquid sources.

7. Do not remain unnecessarily in the region of a radioactive source.

24.8 Nuclear energy

The nucleus of a $^{235}_{92}U$ atom splits into two parts with approximately equal masses when it captures a neutron. The splitting of the nucleus is known as nuclear fission. The products of the fission of one uranium-235 nucleus are:

1. Two new elements, known as fission products. A pair of examples is barium and krypton.

2. Two or three fast-moving neutrons.

3. About 3×10^{-11} J of energy. This energy is released as radiation and as kinetic energy of the neutrons. This kinetic energy is the source of the heat energy obtained from a nuclear reactor.

$$^{235}_{92}U + {}^{1}_{0}n \rightarrow {}^{144}_{56}Ba + {}^{90}_{36}Kr + 2{}^{1}_{0}n$$

This nuclear fission equation shows that the number of nuclear particles (nucleons) is conserved. However, the total mass of the particles on the right-hand side of the equation is slightly less than the total mass on the left. This small mass difference is converted into energy according to the equation:

$$E = mc^2$$

where E is the energy released, m is the mass difference and c is the speed of light ($c = 3 \times 10^8$ m/s).

The fission of one uranium-235 nucleus gives off about 3×10^{-11} J of energy, which is far more than that released by natural radioactive decay.

If the neutrons released by the decay of one uranium-235 nucleus are captured by other nearby uranium-235 nuclei then more fissions occur, resulting in a chain reaction. About 85 per cent of the uranium-235 nuclei which capture a neutron undergo fission, emitting two or three more neutrons. If all these neutrons were captured by uranium-235 nuclei a nuclear explosion would result. This does not happen because in a nuclear reactor it is possible to control the chain reaction. Natural uranium contains only about 0.7 per cent of the isotope $^{235}_{92}$U. 99.3 per cent of the atoms present are of the isotope $^{238}_{92}$U which captures neutrons without fission resulting. Thus in natural uranium the chain reaction would quickly stop.

However, the probability of uranium-235 nuclei capturing neutrons can be increased by slowing the neutrons down. This also reduces the probability of capture by uranium-238 nuclei. The neutrons are slowed down by a material called a moderator, usually water or graphite. Neutrons which have been slowed down are known as thermal neutrons, because they have kinetic energies similar in value to the thermal (heat) energy of the surrounding material.

If the fission process is to be used in a power station, it is necessary to control the chain reaction so that exactly one neutron from the fission of each uranium-235 nucleus causes another similar nucleus to split. If, on average, less than one neutron does so, then the chain reaction will not be self-sustaining. If the number is above one the chain reaction will quickly get out of control and an explosion will result. This control is achieved by the use of control rods of boron, steel or cadmium, which absorb neutrons. The length of the control rods in the uranium core is continually adjusted automatically so that an average of one neutron per nuclear fission causes further splitting.

The heat produced by fission is removed from the reactor core by a coolant which is piped into the core. The pipe containing the coolant passes close to the hot uranium fuel rods and the moderator and much of the heat is absorbed. The heated coolant is then used to run a turbine. From this point onwards a nuclear power station works in the same way as power stations burning oil or coal.

Summary

1   Detectors of radiation rely on the fact that emissions from radioactive sources (e.g. alpha, beta and gamma emissions) all ionize some molecules of any gas through which they pass.

2   An atom consists of a central very small nucleus which contains all the positive charge and most of the mass of the atom. The nucleus is surrounded by electrons (negative charge) in motion. An atom contains an equal number of positive and negative charges.

3   When a substance decays it gives out alpha, beta or gamma radiation or a combination of these.

4   Alpha particles are helium nuclei, beta particles are electrons, and gamma rays are high frequency electromagnetic waves.

5   The half-life of a radioactive substance is the time taken for half the undecayed atoms to decay.

6   It is vital that correct safety procedures are followed when using radioactive materials.

7 The nucleus of a $^{235}_{92}U$ atom splits into two parts of approximately equal masses when it captures a neutron. In addition, 2 or 3 fast moving neutrons and about 3×10^{-11} J of energy are released.

8 If one or more of the neutrons released by the splitting of each $^{235}_{92}U$ nucleus are captured by other $^{235}_{92}U$ nuclei, more splitting (fission) occurs.

9 If on average one of the neutrons released in the splitting of each nucleus causes another similar nucleus to split then a controlled chain reaction results.

10 There are few $^{235}_{92}U$ atoms in naturally occurring uranium. More than 99 per cent of natural uranium are $^{238}_{92}U$ atoms which tend to capture neutrons without fission resulting.

Chapter 25
The Earth and its atmosphere

25.1 Weathering

Look at the photograph in Fig. 25.1. This shows a statue from a church that was built in the 16th century. The statue is about 400 years old. Notice how the stone has been worn away.

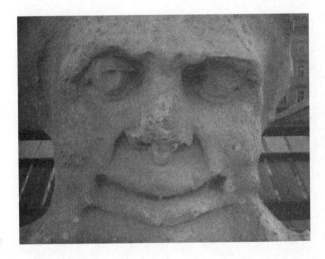

Fig. 25.1 A mediaeval church statue

The church was built from limestone. Limestone reacts very slowly with rain water. Over hundreds of years rain has worn away parts of the statue.

Other rocks, like sandstone and quartz, do not react chemically with rain water, but they still get worn away with time.

When the temperature falls below 0 °C, ice forms. If the ice forms in cracks or crevices, it can break rocks apart because water expands as it freezes.

In mountainous areas, rocks and soil fall down steep slopes into valleys. Fast moving streams pick up some of this material and carry it along causing it to break up even further.

This breaking down and wearing away of rocks by air and water in the environment is called **weathering** or **erosion**.

When the atmosphere is clean, the weathering of rocks takes place very, very slowly. But in polluted air, acid rain causes weathering to occur much more quickly.

25.2 How has soil formed?

Millions of years ago, the Earth's surface was nothing but bare rock. Slowly these rocks were broken up (weathered) by rain, wind, waves and frost into smaller particles. Streams and rivers then carried (**transported**) these smaller particles from one location to another. *These two processes of weathering (erosion) and transport have led to the formation of different types of soil.*

If you look at the edge of a cliff or a pit, you will see how the soil is composed of layers. The top layer is usually the darkest. This is called the **topsoil** where plants and other organisms live. The level below the topsoil is largely stones, clay and gravel. This is called the **subsoil** (Fig. 25.2). Below the subsoil is solid rock.

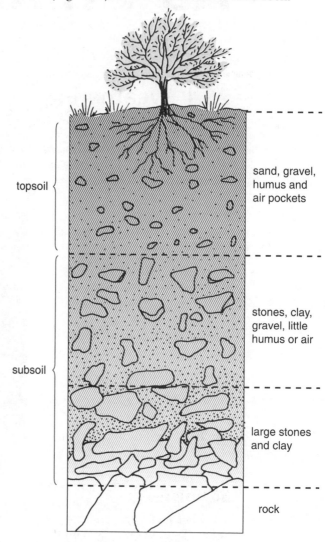

topsoil — sand, gravel, humus and air pockets

subsoil — stones, clay, gravel, little humus or air

large stones and clay

rock

Fig. 25.2 Layers in the soil

What does soil contain?

Soil contains four main constituents:

1. **Rock particles** including sand, gravel, clay, lime and other mineral salts.
2. **Water** – usually absorbed into the solid particles in the soil.
3. **Humus** – formed from the decay of dead plants and animals. Humus is rich in the nutrients and chemicals which plants need to grow. It is fibrous and holds water well. This stops the soil from drying out too fast. Gardeners add compost to soil to increase its humus content.
4. **Air** fills up the spaces between the soil particles. Oxygen in this air is needed for the respiration of living things in the soil and for the decay of humus.

The most fertile soils hold water well, but do not become waterlogged. They contain plenty of plant nutrients and chemicals. This requires a balance between clay (which holds water) and sand (which drains well), plus plenty of humus.

25.3 Rocks in the Earth's crust

When the Earth first cooled, its molten crust solidified to form **igneous rocks**. Over millions of years, two other types of rock were created – **sedimentary rocks** and **metamorphic rocks**. Fig. 25.3 shows how these three types of rock are being formed today.

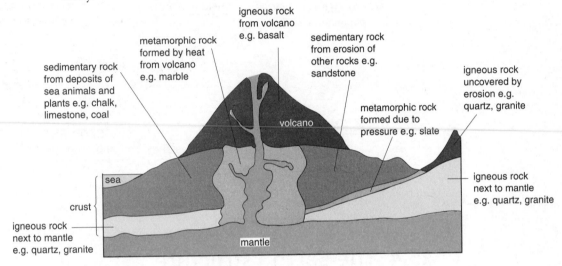

Fig. 25.3 Rocks in the Earth's crust

Igneous rocks

These have formed from the molten rock or **magma** in the Earth's mantle. Some igneous rocks are produced when volcanoes erupt and the lava cools quickly in a matter of days or weeks. This produces rocks, such as basalt, with small crystals. Other igneous rocks, such as granite, diamond and quartz, are formed deep in the Earth's crust next to the mantle. Here the magma cools very slowly over centuries and the rock has much larger crystals.

Sedimentary rocks

When igneous rocks are weathered, they form sediments such as sand and gravel. These sediments may be carried by rivers or ocean currents and deposited elsewhere. As the layers of sediment build up over millions of years, the material below is compressed forming soft rocks such as coal, sandstone and chalk. If the layers are buried deeper, they get converted to harder rocks like limestone. All of these rocks, because they are formed by the build-up of sediment, are known as sedimentary rocks.

Some sedimentary rocks, like sandstone, result from the weathering of other rocks by wind and water. Other sedimentary rocks, such as chalk, limestone and coal, have formed from the remains of dead animals and plants.

Metamorphic rocks

Sedimentary rocks can be changed into harder rocks by enormous pressure or very high temperatures. The new rock has a different structure from the original rock. It is therefore called 'metamorphic rock' from a Greek word meaning 'change of shape'.

Slate and marble are good examples of metamorphic rocks. Slate is formed when clay and mud are subjected to very high temperatures. Marble is formed when limestone comes into contact with hot igneous rock.

In some cases, the temperature gets so high that the metamorphic rocks melt to form magma. This will eventually solidify as igneous rock beginning the rock cycle once again (Fig. 25.4).

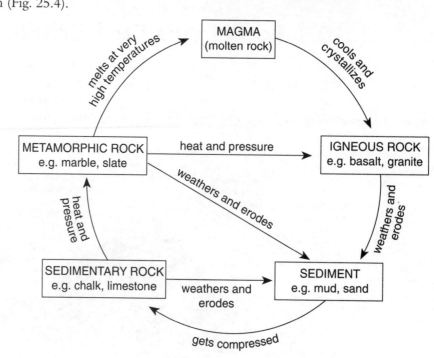

Fig. 25.4 The rock cycle

25.4 The Earth's structure

The Earth is shaped like an orange and its structure is like a badly cracked egg. The 'cracked shell' is the crust, the 'white' is the liquid mantle and the 'yolk' is the core. Evidence for the layered structure of the Earth (Fig. 25.11) comes from the study of earthquakes (see 25.5) and the Earth's magnetic field.

When an earthquake occurs, three kinds of shock waves (**seismic waves**) travel outwards from the centre of the quake (**epicentre**).

1. **Surface waves** roll around the surface of the Earth like waves on the ocean. Surface waves are *transverse* waves. They do most damage to buildings.

2. **Primary waves** or **p-waves** go through the Earth. p-waves are *longitudinal* waves. p-waves travel through the mantle and the core at 5 km/s.

3. **Secondary waves (shear waves)** or **s-waves** also go through the Earth. s-waves are *transverse* waves. They travel through the mantle at 3 km/s, but are reflected when they hit the core.

Seismic waves can be detected using a **seismometer**. A large mass is suspended from a beam. Even a slight earth tremor will cause some movement of the suspended mass. This movement can be charted using a pen recorder. Scientists have obtained evidence for the Earth's internal structure from the records of p-waves and s-waves on seismometers.

s-waves are not detected by seismometers at an angle greater than 105° from the epicentre of the quake. p-waves are also *not* detected after 105°, but they reappear again at 140°. This suggests that:

- s-waves cannot pass through the Earth's dense core,
- p-waves are refracted by the core.

The Earth has a strong magnetic field. Scientists think that this magnetism exists because the Earth's core is made of iron. Rocks in the Earth's crust and in lava, which contain iron, also take on this magnetism as they solidify.

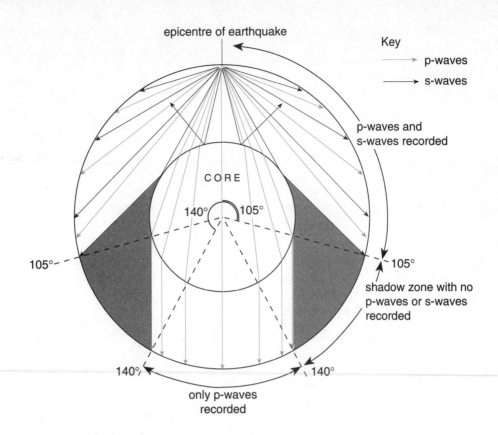

25.5 Plate tectonics

The Earth's crust has cracked into huge sections called **plates** (Fig. 25.6). These vast plates move very slowly due to convection currents in the liquid mantle below the crust.

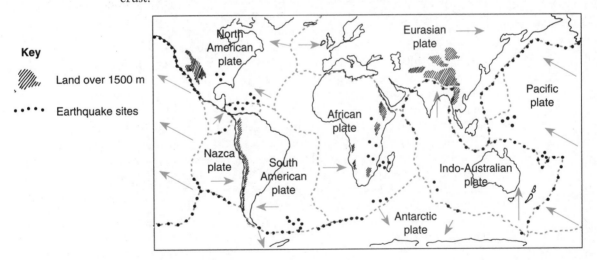

Fig. 25.6 The Earth's crust is like the shell of a cracked egg. Huge sections called plates cover the Earth's surface. Most earthquakes and volcanoes occur near the edges of the plates

When the plates slide past each other, move apart or push towards each other, various things can happen.

When two plates slide past each other

Stresses and strains build up in the Earth's crust. This may cause the plates to bend. In some cases, the stresses and strains are released suddenly. The Earth moves and the ground shakes violently in an **earthquake** (Fig. 25.7(a)). During an earthquake, the ground breaks as the earth moves. These breaks in the ground are called **faults** (Fig. 25.7(b)).

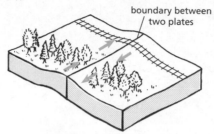 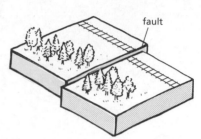

(a) Plates in the Earth's crust are bent as they slide past each other in opposite directions. The earth and rocks are displaced sideways.

(b) Stresses in the bent planes are suddenly released as a break appears in the earth. The ground shakes (an earthquake) and a fault has formed.

Fig. 25.7 How an earthquake occurs

When plates move apart

Cracks appear in the Earth's crust. Hot molten rock escapes through the cracks and erupts as a volcano in a shower of dust, smoke and burning liquid. As the plates move further apart, surface rocks sink forming vertical **faults**. When two vertical faults occur alongside each other, rift valleys are formed.

Most of the volcanoes in the world have never been seen. They lie deep under the oceans where plates are moving apart. An important example of this is the submerged ocean ridge along the boundary between the North and South American plates and the Eurasian and African plates (Fig. 25.6). This ridge extends down the centre of the Atlantic Ocean from the Arctic to the Antarctic. It has formed as vast amounts of lava pour out from volcanoes onto the ocean floor.

When plates push towards each other and collide

Rocks are squeezed together. Along the western edge of South America, the Nazca plate is being pushed against the South American plate (Fig. 25.6). Here the ocean crust in the Nazca plate is being forced beneath the advancing South American plate. This is pushing up the landmass and creating the Andes Mountains.

The last phase in the tectonic cycle occurs when two landmasses collide and the ocean between them disappears. When this happens, layers of the Earth's crust are squeezed into **folds**. Over millions of years, mountains and valleys are formed. This happened when the Indo-Australian plate moved north and collided with the Eurasian plate. The ancient Tethys Ocean disappeared and the Himalayas formed.

Notice how plate tectonics contributes to the recycling of rocks. As plates move apart, lava pours out onto the Earth's surface forming igneous rock. This igneous rock begins to weather, producing sediment for the formation of sedimentary rocks. When plates collide, the land is pushed upwards forming mountains. These mountains are eroded by wind and water and in a hundred million years they will have gone. Mountain ranges have come and gone several times in the 4600 million years since the Earth began.

25.6 The theory of plate tectonics

The theory of plate tectonics was put forward in 1912 by the German scientist Alfred Wegener.

- Wegener noticed the way in which the east coast of South America could fit into the west coast of Africa.
- He also knew of evidence to suggest that a major ice sheet had once covered most of southern Africa, southern Australia and India.

Wegener suggested that all the continents once formed part of a supercontinent which he called **Pangaea**, from a Greek word meaning 'all the Earth' (Fig. 25.8). About 200 million years ago, part of Pangaea lay near the South Pole. Since then, the continents have been drifting apart. Wegener explained this by saying that the continents were part of giant blocks or plates floating and moving on the liquid mantle below the Earth's crust. This was his theory of plate tectonics.

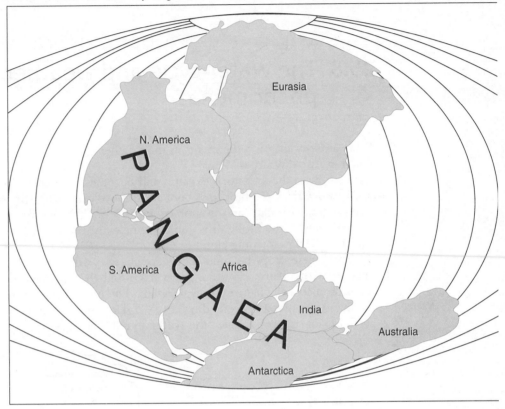

Fig. 25.8 Pangaea – the Earth 200 million years ago

The occurrence and explanation of volcanoes, earthquakes, faults and folds (see Unit 25.5) supports Wegener's theory. The latest evidence to support his theory has been obtained from lasers mounted on satellites. These lasers have been able to measure changes of as little as 2 or 3 cm per year in the movement of continents, the width of oceans and the height of mountains.

25.7 Winds, weather and climate

Every time the wind blows we are aware that the air is moving. These movements of the air cause winds, rain and clouds which affect climate and weather. We can describe the **weather** using measurements of **temperature**, **rainfall**, **wind speed** and **wind direction**.

Each part of the world has its own pattern of weather. Very often, this pattern is the same from one year to the next. This general pattern in the weather is called the **climate**.

The climate in different parts of the Earth is greatly affected by the movement of large masses of air. These large masses of air are called **airstreams**.

The air above an ocean contains lots of water vapour. When this air approaches the land and rises, it cools. If the water vapour is cooled sufficiently, it will condense and then fall as rain. So, in those parts of the world where airstreams move over oceans there is often plenty of rain.

In contrast to this, the air above large land masses usually contains very little water vapour. This means that those parts of the world where airstreams move large distances over the land usually have low rainfall.

In general, *climate is controlled by the movements of airstreams over very large distances.* On the other hand, *weather from day to day is controlled by smaller bodies of air.* Because of this, the weather can change rapidly in some parts of the world, such as the UK.

25.8 The water cycle and weather phenomena

There are four major components to the weather:
● Sun ● Air ● Wind ● Water

The Sun heats the air which expands and becomes less dense. So, the warm air rises as convection currents. This allows cool air to move in causing winds.

Heat from the Sun also evaporates water from the oceans. As this warm moist air rises, it cools. If the moist air is cooled sufficiently, the water vapour in it will condense into tiny droplets forming clouds.

When these drops become large enough, they fall as rain. This is sometimes called **precipitation**. If the clouds are very high and the temperature falls below 0 °C, the water droplets will change into ice crystals. These will fall as snow or hail.

This cycle of water from the Earth's surface into the clouds and then back to the Earth as rain or snow is called the **water cycle** (Fig. 25.9).

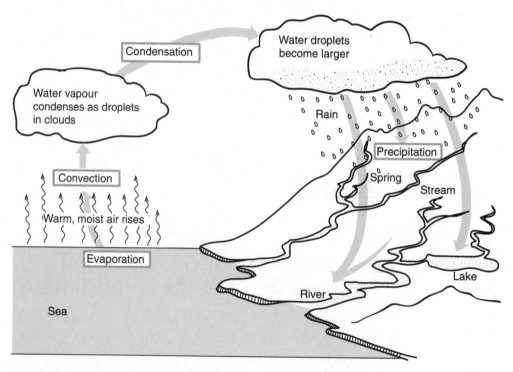

Fig. 25.9 The water cycle

Other weather phenomena such as fogs and frosts are also caused by energy transfer processes involving the Sun and the atmosphere.

During the day, radiation from the Sun causes water to evaporate into the air from rivers and oceans. The warmer the atmosphere becomes, the more water vapour collects in the air.

At night, the Earth and atmosphere cool quite rapidly. If the temperature falls sufficiently, water vapour condenses in the air as tiny droplets of **mist**. If more water vapour condenses, the mist gets thicker forming **fog**. Sometimes the water vapour condenses so much that droplets form on windows, grass and other cold surfaces as **dew**. In winter months, the temperature may fall below 0 °C. When this happens, the water solidifies as ice and a **frost** occurs.

25.9 Water supplies

All living things need water. Every day your body needs about two litres (3½ pints) of water to replace the water lost in urine, in sweat and when you breathe. In some ways, water is more important to us than food. We can survive about fifty or sixty days without food, but only five to ten days without water.

In addition to the water we must drink, we also need water for personal washing, clothes washing, dish washing, toilet flushing, etc. Every time you flush the toilet, about ten litres of water are used. Industry uses even larger amounts of water. Most of this water is used for cooling. For example, a large power station uses about five million litres of water for cooling every day. This water need not be pure, so it can be taken from rivers or from the sea.

The public water supply which comes to our homes is, of course, treated (cleaned) by the water companies. The source of this water is usually a river, a lake or an underground well. The main stages in the treatment of our public water supply are shown in Fig. 25.10.

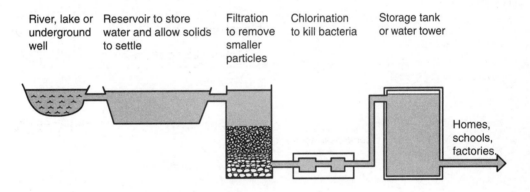

Fig. 25.10 The main stages in the treatment of our public water supply

25.10 Origins of the Earth and atmosphere

4500 million years ago, the Earth was a mass of molten rock which has slowly cooled down over millions of years. During this period, heavier metals sunk to the centre of the Earth forming a **core** of dense molten iron at about 4000 °C (Fig. 25.11). This core is surrounded by less dense, rocky material in the **mantle** at temperatures between 1500 and 4000 °C. Lighter materials remained on the surface forming a thin **crust** about 50 km thick.

Whilst the Earth was still forming, the **atmosphere** above its surface was mainly hydrogen and helium. These gases could escape from the Earth into outer space. As the molten, volcanic surface cooled, other gases were added. These included water vapour, carbon dioxide, methane and nitrogen.

As the temperature dropped still further, water vapour condensed to form rivers, lakes and oceans. When plants appeared, 3500 million years ago, oxygen was formed from water and carbon dioxide by photosynthesis and used up during respiration.

Flammable gases such as hydrogen and methane burnt in this oxygen forming more water and carbon dioxide.

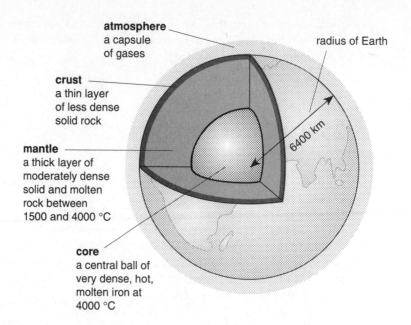

atmosphere
a capsule
of gases

radius of Earth

crust
a thin layer
of less dense
solid rock

6400 km

mantle
a thick layer of
moderately dense
solid and molten
rock between
1500 and 4000 °C

core
a central ball of
very dense, hot,
molten iron at
4000 °C

Fig. 25.11 Layers of the Earth. Note how the temperature and density of the layers decrease as you move towards the Earth's surface

In time, animals evolved and used the oxygen for respiration. This further helped to keep a balance between the production and removal of oxygen and carbon dioxide in the atmosphere.

The composition of the atmosphere has remained more or less constant for the last 500 million years. The main constituents are **nitrogen** and **oxygen** (Table 25.1) with smaller amounts of **noble gases**, **carbon dioxide** and **water vapour**.

Table 25.1 Gases present in dry air

Nitrogen	78.07%
Oxygen	20.97%
Argon	0.93%
Carbon dioxide	0.03%
Noble gases (helium, neon, krypton and xenon)	Traces

The Earth is the only planet in our solar system with oxygen in its atmosphere and surface water in rivers, lakes and oceans. Other planets such as Mars do, however, have some water vapour and polar ice caps.

25.11 Weather maps

At one time, weather forecasts were very unreliable. Today, meteorologists can measure atmospheric pressure, wind speeds, temperature and humidity (the amount of water vapour in the air). These measurements combined with photos from satellites above the Earth have made weather forecasts much more accurate.

Look at the weather map in Fig. 25.12. This is similar to those you have seen on TV or in newspapers.

The thin lines on the map link places with the same atmospheric pressure. These lines are called **isobars**. If the isobars are extended far enough they form closed curves which look like contour lines. When the isobars enclose a region of low pressure (L), the system is called a **depression** or a **cyclone**. If they enclose a region of high pressure (H), the system is an **anticyclone**.

In areas of high pressure, the airstreams are moving down and away from the area. This usually brings fine weather. In areas of low pressure, airstreams are usually rising

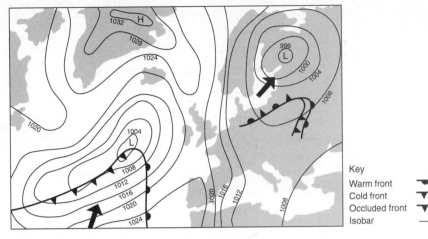

Fig. 25.12 The Atlantic weather map at noon on a June day

and moving towards the area. If this air contains water vapour, it may condense and fall as rain.

Meteorologists express pressure in **millibars**. One millibar is 100 N/m². Atmospheric pressure is usually about 1000 millibars. On a weather map, the isobars are usually drawn at intervals of 4 or 8 millibars.

When the isobars are close together, atmospheric pressure changes rapidly over a short distance. Consequently there are high winds as the air moves rapidly from a region of high pressure to one of low pressure. When the isobars are widely spaced, the wind speed is usually light and variable.

On weather maps, wind directions are shown by arrows. You might expect winds to blow straight across the isobars from areas of high pressure to areas of low pressure. This simple pattern is, however, complicated by the Earth's own rotation. In the Northern hemisphere winds tend to blow clockwise around high-pressure areas and anticlockwise around depressions.

In Britain, the weather is largely dictated by airstreams from the North Atlantic. Depressions form over the Atlantic Ocean and then travel towards the north-east. The depressions usually have associated **fronts** or boundaries separating regions of air at different temperatures. A **warm front** separates cold air from advancing warm air. A **cold front** separates warmer air from advancing cold air.

Generally, the cold front of the depression overtakes the warm front, because the warm air rises above the cold air. As the warm moist air rises, it cools. This causes water vapour to condense giving rain. Eventually, the warm and cold fronts unite forming an **occluded front**. When this happens, the pressure rises and the depression dies away.

Summary

1   The breaking down and wearing away of rocks by air and water in the environment is called **weathering** or **erosion**.

2   The movement of sediment from one location to another by streams and rivers is called **transport**.

3   The processes of weathering and transport have led to different types of soil.

4   Soil contains four main constituents – rock particles, water, humus and air.

5   **Igneous rocks** have formed from the molten rock or **magma** in the Earth's mantle.

6   **Sedimentary rocks** have formed from sediments as a result of the pressure of overlying materials.

7   **Metamorphic rocks** have formed from sedimentary rocks by the action of enormous pressure or very high temperatures.

8   When an earthquake occurs, **seismic waves** travel outwards from the centre of the quake (**epicentre**).

9   The Earth's crust has cracked into huge sections called **plates**.

10 **Earthquakes** occur when two plates slide past each other, bend and then suddenly move into new positions. This produces breaks in the ground called **faults**.

11 **Volcanoes** occur when the plates move apart and cracks appear in the Earth's crust. Hot molten rocks can then escape through the cracks.

12 When two plates push towards each other, layers in the Earth's crust are squeezed into **folds**.

13 The Earth has a dense **core** of molten iron at 4000 °C. This is surrounded by less dense, rocky material in the **mantle** at temperatures between 1500 and 4000 °C. Lighter materials form a thin surface **crust** about 50 km thick.

14 The **weather** can be described using measurements of temperature, rainfall, wind speed and wind direction.

15 The general pattern in the weather is called the **climate**.

16 In general, climate is controlled by movements of airstreams over very large distances. Weather from day to day is controlled by smaller bodies of air.

17 The cycle of water from the Earth's surface into the clouds and back to the Earth as rain or snow is called the **water cycle**.

18 On a weather map, lines joining places with the same atmospheric pressure are called **isobars**.

19 When isobars enclose a region of low pressure, the system is called a **depression** or a **cyclone**. When isobars enclose a region of high pressure, the system is an **anticyclone**.

20 Atmospheric pressure is given in **millibars**. 1 millibar = 100 N/m^2. Atmospheric pressure is usually about 1000 millibars.

21 A **warm front** separates colder air from advancing warm air. A **cold front** separates warmer air from advancing cold air. When warm and cold fronts unite, they form an **occluded front**.

Chapter 26
The Earth's place in the universe

26.1 Introduction

Astronomy, the study of the heavens, has always fascinated men and women. Early star watchers used their eyes. Later, binoculars and telescopes gave a clearer picture. Nowadays, telescopes that detect invisible radiowaves from outer space are providing us with even more information. Since Ed Aldrin and Neil Armstrong landed on the Moon on 21 July 1969, our horizons have widened still further. Our colonization of other planets is becoming a possibility.

26.2 What are stars?

Looking up into the sky on a clear night you will see thousands of stars. Stars were formed and continue to be formed by the compression of gas and dust scattered throughout space. Stars emit light as a result of reactions like those in nuclear reactors.

The **Sun** is a star. It is the nearest star to Earth and is at the centre of our **solar system**.

Clusters of stars group together to form **galaxies** and billions of galaxies make up the whole **universe**. The Sun and the solar system are part of the **Milky Way** galaxy (Fig. 26.1). There are approximately 100 000 million stars in the Milky Way and the Sun is just one of them. It would take 100 000 light years to cross the Milky Way (i.e. 100 000 years travelling at the speed of light). Light can travel about 10^{16} metres in one year alone. Just imagine how small the Earth really is compared to the size of the universe.

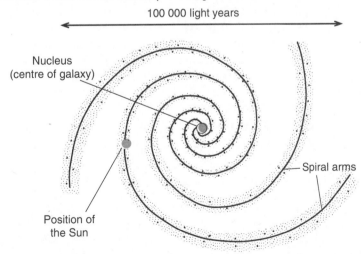

Fig. 26.1 The Milky Way galaxy

26.3 The Sun

Without the Sun there would be no life on Earth. The Sun provides light and warmth for photosynthesis, enabling plants to grow. Fig. 26.2 shows the structure of the Sun.

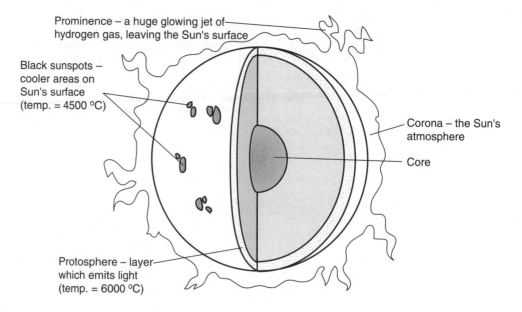

Prominence – a huge glowing jet of hydrogen gas, leaving the Sun's surface

Black sunspots – cooler areas on Sun's surface (temp. = 4500 °C)

Corona – the Sun's atmosphere

Core

Protosphere – layer which emits light (temp. = 6000 °C)

Fig. 26.2 The structure of the Sun

The high temperatures on the Sun are caused by nuclear fusion processes which occur in its core. During these nuclear processes heavy hydrogen (deuterium, ^2_1H) atoms join together (fuse) to form helium (^4_2He) atoms.

$$^2_1H \quad + \quad {}^2_1H \quad \rightarrow \quad {}^4_2He \quad + \quad heat \quad + \quad light$$

At the same time, enormous amounts of heat and light are emitted and the temperature in the core of the Sun reaches 15 000 000 °C.

Theories about the universe

Early Greek philosophers watched the Sun, the Moon and other planets carefully. They recorded their movements across the sky. In AD 150, Ptolemy suggested that the Earth was at the centre of the universe and the Sun and stars revolved around it.

A heliocentric theory, in which the Earth and planets revolve around the Sun, was proposed by Aristarchus in the third century BC. Copernicus provided some evidence for this theory in the fifteenth century. As more and more evidence was obtained, it became clear that:

- the Earth and other planets move around the Sun,
- the Earth rotates on a tilted axis once every 24 hours.

26.4 Days, nights and seasons

Day and night

As the Earth rotates on its axis (Fig. 26.3), different parts of the Earth face towards the Sun. When we are in the light, it is daytime. When we are on the side of the Earth away from the Sun, we are in darkness and it is night. It takes 24 hours for the Earth to rotate once on its axis. So, day and night are repeated every 24 hours.

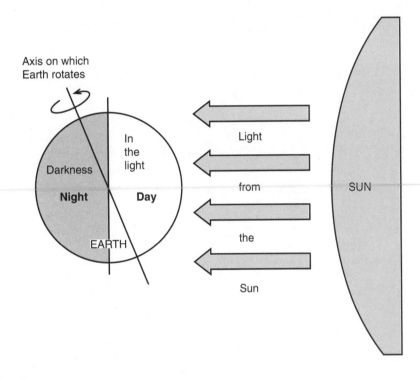

Fig. 26.3 Day and night

Seasons

The Earth revolves around the Sun as well as rotating on its axis. The seasons occur because the Earth's axis is tilted at $23\frac{1}{2}°$ to the vertical (Fig. 26.4). When the Northern hemisphere is tilted towards the Sun, it is summer there and winter in the Southern

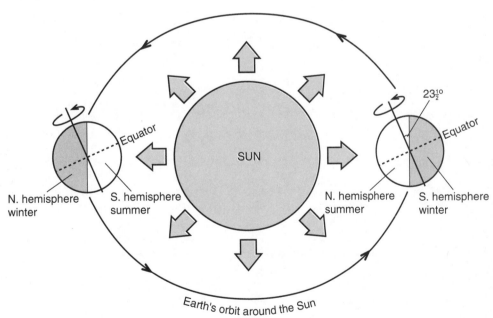

Fig. 26.4 Explaining the seasons

hemisphere. When the Northern hemisphere is tilted away from the Sun, it is winter there and summer in the Southern hemisphere.

It takes $365\frac{1}{4}$ days for the Earth to travel in orbit once around the Sun. So, $365\frac{1}{4}$ days is one **year**. After one year, the seasons are repeated.

Day length

Notice in Fig. 26.4 that when the Northern hemisphere has its summer, the days are longer as more of it is in sunlight than the Southern hemisphere. At this time, more of the Southern hemisphere is in darkness so it has long winter nights.

26.5 Planets and the solar system

Our solar system consists of the Sun and nine planets (Fig. 26.5). Notice that there are four planets (Mercury, Venus, Earth and Mars) relatively close to the Sun, and five planets (Jupiter, Saturn, Uranus, Neptune and Pluto) further away. All of the planets move in elliptical orbits in the same direction around the Sun. With the exception of Pluto, all the planets lie in much the same plane. Pluto's orbit is at an angle to this plane.

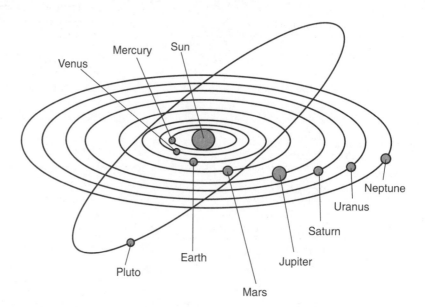

Fig. 26.5 The planets in our solar system

26.6 Gravity and gravitational forces

Experiments have shown that gravitational forces act between all masses. So, there is a gravitational force between you and everything else in the universe. However, gravitational forces get stronger if the objects involved have larger masses or if they get closer. The largest object, close to you, is the Earth. Because of this, the gravitational force between you and the Earth may be 500 N or more. This, of course, is your **weight**. Even if you sit close to one of your friends, the gravitational force between the pair of you will only be about one millionth of a newton.

The Sun contains 99.8% of the mass of our solar system. Because of this, it exerts very strong gravitational forces. These forces are strong enough to hold the planets in orbit even though they are moving at high speed.

26.7 The origin of the solar system

It is difficult to imagine how our solar system came about. Astronomers now agree that the Sun and planets were formed about 4600 million years ago. Fig. 26.6 shows the main stages in the process which lasted millions of years.

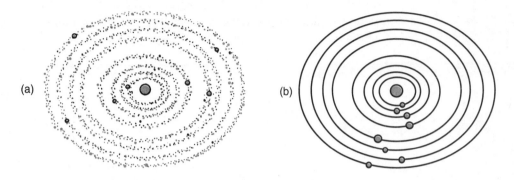

Fig. 26.6 Stages in the formation of our solar system

At first, a cloud of gas and dust rotated around a central heavy core like a flat disc. Dust particles attracted each other by gravity, building up the core and other large spheres within the disc (Fig. 26.6(a)).

Eventually, a small number of dense spheres resulted (Fig. 26.6(b)). The central sphere with the greatest concentration of mass was the Sun and the remainder gave rise to the planets. Gases formed in the atmospheres surrounding these planets.

On planets close to the Sun, where it is hotter, most of the gases have evaporated. This has left small rocky planets (Mercury, Venus, Earth and Mars) with iron cores (Table 26.1).

Further from the Sun, where it is colder, the gases have not evaporated fully leaving crystals of methane, ammonia and ice with the gases helium and hydrogen. Because of this, Jupiter, Saturn, Uranus and Neptune are much larger planets with small rocky cores surrounded by vast quantities of gas (Table 26.1).

Table 26.1 Data concerning the planets in our solar system

Planet	Average distance of planet from the Sun (millions of km)	Diameter of planet relative to diameter of the Earth	Average surface temp (°C)
Mercury	58	0.4	450
Venus	108	1	500
Earth	150	1	20
Mars	228	0.5	−40
Jupiter	778	11	−150
Saturn	1427	9.4	−160
Uranus	2870	4	−220
Neptune	4497	3.9	−230
Pluto	5900	0.5	−230

Pluto, furthest from the Sun, is thought to be a satellite of Neptune which has escaped and moved into its own orbit. It is very small and rocky.

Notice that the conditions on a planet depend on two key factors:

● **its nearness to the Sun**, which determines the surface temperature and the evaporation of volatile substances,

● **its relative size**, which determines the gravitational pull on any atmosphere it might have.

In general, the small planets have little or no atmosphere due to their small gravitational attraction.

26.8 The Earth and its Moon

The Moon orbits the Earth once a month. It is therefore a satellite or planet of the Earth. Experiments during the American Apollo missions to the Moon in the 1960s have shown that there are no living organisms on the Moon.

At any moment, half of the Moon is lit up by the Sun, and the other half is in shadow. From the Earth we can see only the illuminated side. That is why we see the Moon in various phases or shapes (Fig. 26.7).

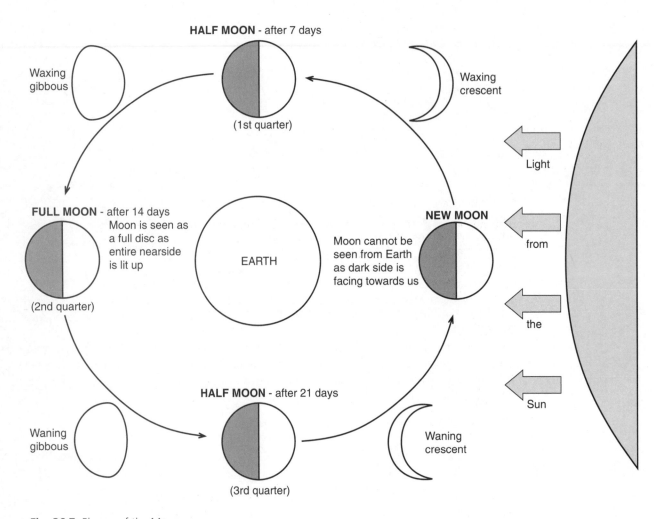

Fig. 26.7 Phases of the Moon

Along the line dividing the illuminated and dark sides of the Moon, the Sun's rays cast long shadows. These shadows highlight details of the lunar landscape such as craters and mountain ranges. The craters were caused by meteors (rocks in space) colliding with the Moon whilst it was still molten.

Tides

Tides occur due to the gravitational pull of the Moon on the oceans (and to a lesser extent the pull of the Sun). As the Moon orbits the Earth, its gravitational pull draws the oceans towards it (Fig. 26.8). This causes the sea to rise giving high tides at points A and B and low tides at points X and Y.

At certain times, the Sun and Moon are both in line with the Earth (see Fig. 26.7). When this happens, there are extra high tides called **spring tides**. At other times, the Sun and Moon are at right angles to the Earth (see Fig. 26.7). When this happens, their gravitational pulls tend to cancel each other out. This produces lower high tides called **neap tides**.

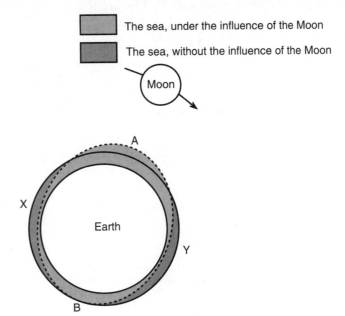

Fig. 26.8 The effect of the Moon on our tides

Comets

The movements of comets can also be explained using the idea of gravitational forces. Comets travel around the Sun in very long, elliptical orbits. They reappear every few years. Their orbits can be plotted and their arrival in our night sky can be predicted by astronomers. They are often spectacular to look at with bright heads and long sparkly tails, thousands of kilometres long (Fig. 26.9).

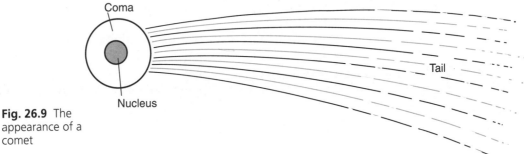

Fig. 26.9 The appearance of a comet

The comet's nucleus is thought to be rocky material covered with vast amounts of frozen gases. The coma is produced when the comet gets close to the Sun, causing some of the frozen gases to vaporize.

Each comet is named after the person who discovered it. The most famous comet is probably Halley's Comet, named after Edmond Halley in 1720. Halley used the idea of gravity and the movement of planets to predict when his comet would be visible again from the Earth. He was widely acclaimed when the comet reappeared almost exactly on the date he had predicted.

26.9 Our exploration of space

Over the centuries, astronomers have obtained much information about planets and stars by observing them from the Earth. More detailed information is now obtained by launching rockets into space. The launch and the orbit of any spacecraft are governed by the laws of gravity. Fig. 26.10 explains how a rocket can be launched to orbit the Moon.

Rockets have enabled scientists to study 'near space' very successfully. However, astronomers soon realized that artificial satellites would be a more thorough and economical way of studying space. These satellites could be carried into space by rockets and then set in stable orbits around the Earth or other planets. Satellites have already provided detailed photographs of the planets and they are also used to relay television pictures across the world.

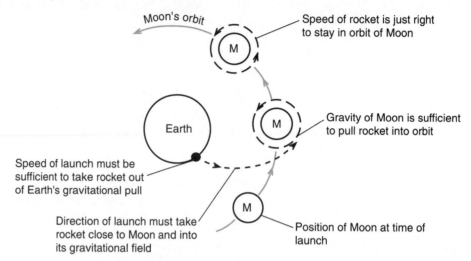

Fig. 26.10 Launching a rocket to orbit the Moon

More recently space stations have been built and launched. Scientists can live in these for several months, carrying out experiments which could not be done on Earth. The American Space Shuttle has reduced the cost of sending crews to space stations. It flies back to Earth like an aeroplane and can be used again and again.

Scientists in space stations have studied the Sun and stars in detail. They have also used the weightless conditions in space to purify vaccines and to make ultralightweight foamed steels from metals and glass.

Although colonization of the Moon is possible, there are many problems to overcome:

- There is no air and no water on the Moon.
- The expense of travelling to the Moon would be considerable. Colonists would need to spend significant lengths of time there before returning to Earth.
- Food supplies could not be carried to the Moon from the Earth. It would be necessary to grow plants and produce food there.

Ideally a lunar station would be self-supporting, recycling air, water and food.

26.10 The life cycle of stars

Stars are not permanent. They have 'birth', 'life' and 'death'. Our Sun is a middle-aged star which is about ten thousand million years old. In another ten thousand million years, it will stop emitting light and die.

A piece of coal is normally black. When it is heated it gradually changes colour to dull red and then bright yellow. In the same way, stars indicate their temperature and age by their brightness and colour (see Fig. 26.11).

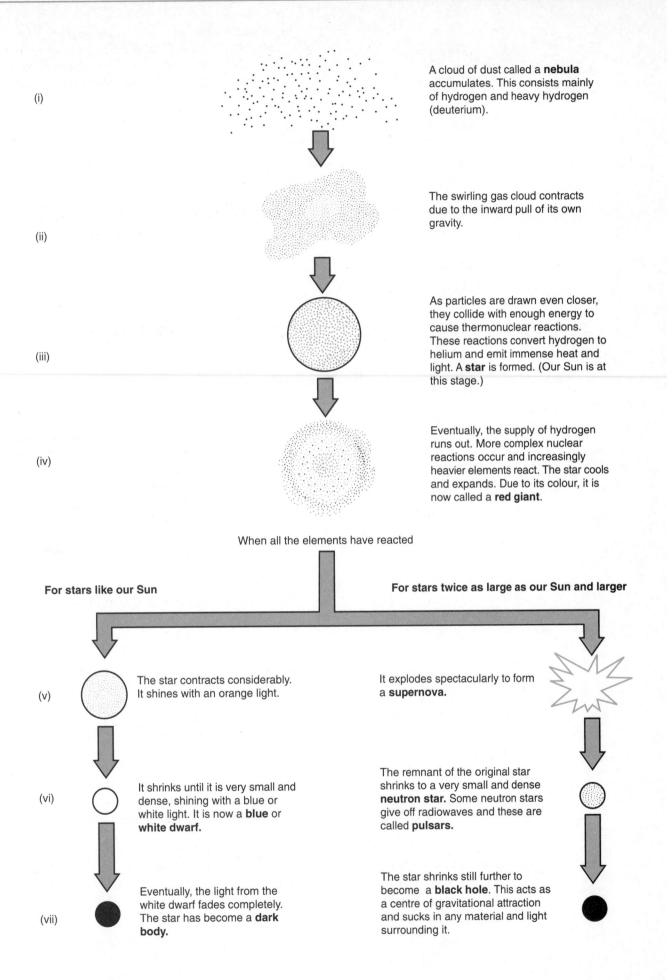

(i) A cloud of dust called a **nebula** accumulates. This consists mainly of hydrogen and heavy hydrogen (deuterium).

(ii) The swirling gas cloud contracts due to the inward pull of its own gravity.

(iii) As particles are drawn even closer, they collide with enough energy to cause thermonuclear reactions. These reactions convert hydrogen to helium and emit immense heat and light. A **star** is formed. (Our Sun is at this stage.)

(iv) Eventually, the supply of hydrogen runs out. More complex nuclear reactions occur and increasingly heavier elements react. The star cools and expands. Due to its colour, it is now called a **red giant**.

When all the elements have reacted

For stars like our Sun

For stars twice as large as our Sun and larger

(v) The star contracts considerably. It shines with an orange light.

It explodes spectacularly to form a **supernova**.

(vi) It shrinks until it is very small and dense, shining with a blue or white light. It is now a **blue** or **white dwarf.**

The remnant of the original star shrinks to a very small and dense **neutron star.** Some neutron stars give off radiowaves and these are called **pulsars.**

(vii) Eventually, the light from the white dwarf fades completely. The star has become a **dark body.**

The star shrinks still further to become a **black hole**. This acts as a centre of gravitational attraction and sucks in any material and light surrounding it.

Fig. 26.11 The stages in the life cycle of a star

Summary

1   **Day and night** result from the Earth's rotation on its axis.

2   **Seasons** and the varying lengths of days result from the tilt of the Earth's axis and the Earth's movement around the Sun.

3   **The phases** (shapes) **of the Moon** result from the Moon's movement around the Earth.

4   Our **solar system** consists of the Sun and nine planets. In order from the Sun these planets are Mercury, Venus, Earth, Mars, Jupiter, Saturn, Uranus, Neptune and Pluto.

5   **Gravitational forces** hold the planets in orbit around the Sun.

6   The Sun is a **star**. Stars are immense volumes of hot reacting gas and dust.

7   Clusters of stars make up **galaxies** and billions of galaxies make up the whole **universe**.

8   The **conditions on a planet** depend on two key factors:
    ● its nearness to the Sun and
    ● its relative size.

9   Tides occur due to the gravitational pull of the Moon (and to a lesser extent the Sun) on the oceans.

10 Stars have a life cycle. They begin as a cloud of dust (**nebula**) which contracts, causing thermonuclear reactions, to form a **star**. Eventually the supply of hydrogen runs out and the star cools and contracts.

Self-test questions

This section contains a selection of multiple choice questions and is designed to test your knowledge and understanding of the material in this book. Before attempting these questions you should read about tackling multiple choice questions on p.11.

Questions (answers p.159)

Type 1
Each question below has five possible answers labelled A, B, C, D, E. For each question select the one which is the best answer. Within the group of questions each answer may be used once, more than once or not at all.

Questions 1–3

    A newton per second
    B kilogram metre per second
    C newton metre per second
    D newton metre
    E kilogram metre per second^2

Which one of the above is a unit in which each of the following physical quantities might be measured?

1   momentum

2   work

3   power

Questions 4–7

The graph shows how the velocity of a moving object starting from rest changes with time.

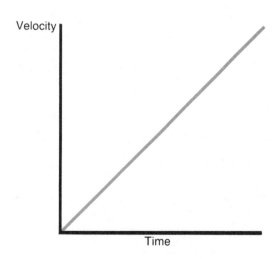

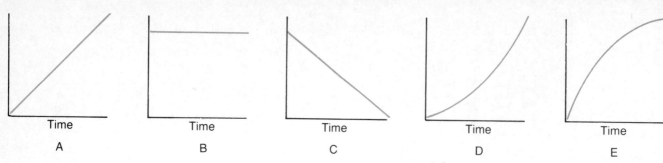

Time	Time	Time	Time	Time
A	B	C	D	E

Select from the graphs A–E above the one which most nearly represents the shape of each of the following graphs for the moving object.

4 acceleration against time

5 the force acting on the body against time

6 distance travelled against time

Questions 7–11

The following are five properties of an object made of the same metal throughout.

   A mass   B volume   C weight   D density   E surface area

Which of the properties

7 is a vector quantity?

8 would change if the body were taken to the moon, its temperature remaining constant?

9 is calculated from two of the other properties?

10 would not change if the body were cut in half and only one half were considered?

11 has units of kilogram metre per second^2?

Questions 12–14

The following are five units

   A kilogram   D newton
   B kilogram metre per second   E metre per second^2
   C joule

Which of the above units is suitable for measuring each of the following quantities?

12 the kinetic energy of a cricket ball

13 the momentum of a cricket ball

14 the weight of a cricket ball

Questions 15–17

Which of the following words best describes the particles in question?

   A protons   B molecules   C ions   D electrons   E neutrons

15 carbon dioxide gas at room temperature

16 particles emitted from a hot filament in the tube of a cathode ray oscilloscope

17 alpha particles emitted by a radioactive substance

Questions 18–20

Five types of radiation are listed below.

   A ultraviolet radiation   D beta radiation
   B infrared radiation   E ultrasonic radiation
   C gamma radiation

Select the type of radiation to which each of the following applies.

18 The wavelength is slightly shorter than that of visible light and it can cause certain materials to fluoresce.

19 The wavelength is extremely short, much shorter than that of visible light, and it can be emitted from the nucleus of an atom.

20 The wavelength is slightly longer than that of visible light and it may be used for heating.

Questions 21 and 22

Resistors of 1 ohm, 1 ohm and 2 ohms are connected in arrangements lettered A to E below.

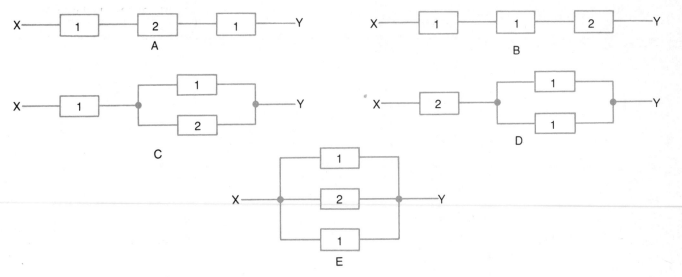

21 Which arrangement has the smallest total resistance between *X* and *Y*?

22 Which arrangement would have the largest current through the 2 ohm resistor when a potential difference is applied between *X* and *Y* ?

Type 2
Each of the following questions or incomplete statements is followed by five suggested answers labelled A, B, C, D, E. Select the best answer in each case.

23 Which of the following is measured in newtons?

    A energy   B force   C power   D pressure   E work

24 Which of the graphs best represents the velocity–time graph of a ball thrown vertically upwards to a considerable height and which then returns to the thrower?

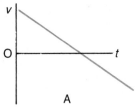 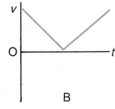 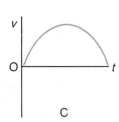 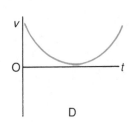 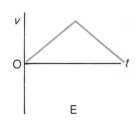

Questions 25 and 26

A car takes 5 seconds to accelerate uniformly from rest until it reaches a speed of 10 metres per second.

25 What is its acceleration?

    A 0.5 m/s^2 B 2 m/s^2 C 5 m/s^2 D 10 m/s^2 E 50 m/s^2

26 How far does it travel during the 5 seconds?

    A 2 m   B 5 m   C 10 m   D 25 m   E 50 m

27 A 5 kg mass is travelling with a speed of 5 m/s. It is brought to rest in 0.5 s. What is the average force acting on it to bring it to rest?

    A 50 N   B 25 N   C 10 N   D 2.5 N   E 0.5 N

28 An astronaught goes to the moon where the gravitational attraction is less than on the Earth. Which one of the following correctly describes the change(s) in his mass and/or weight?

	Mass	*Weight*
A	increases	unchanged
B	unchanged	unchanged
C	unchanged	decreases
D	decreases	unchanged
E	decreases	decreases

29 A car of mass 800 kg which is moving east at 50 m/s collides head on with a van of mass 1600 kg which is moving west at 10 m/s. What will the wreck do if the vehicles stick together?

A be stationary   D move east at 10 m/s
B move east at 20 m/s   E move west at 10 m/s
C move west at 20 m/s

30 8 kg of water is tipped from a bucket at the top of a building of height 200 m and forms a static pool on the ground. What will be its change in energy?

A 1 600 000 J gain   D 16 000 J loss
B 16 000 J gain   E 1 600 000 J loss
C no change

31 Which of the following is the unit of work?

A watt   D newton/metre
B joule   E metre
C newton

32 A ship is sailing slowly due east, and a passenger is on the deck at *P*. In the diagram the points *A*, *B*, *C*, *D* and *E* are marked on the deck. Towards which of these points should the passenger walk at a suitable speed in order to move due north?

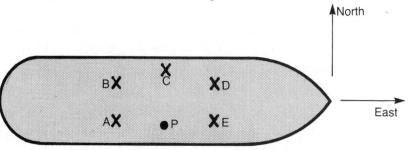

33 What is the value of the force *F* if the beam shown in the diagram is balanced?

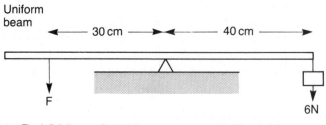

A 3 N   B 4.5 N   C 6 N   D 8 N   E 10 N

34 A metal cube, with each side 2 cm in length, has a density of 8 g/cm³. What is the mass of the cube?

A 2g   B 4 g   C 8 g   D 16 g   E 64 g

35 A boy of mass 40 kg balances evenly on two stilts, each having an area of 8 cm² in contact with the ground. What is the pressure exerted by one stilt?

A 50 N/cm²   B 40 N/cm²   C 25 N/cm²   D 5 N/cm²   E 2.5 N/cm²

36 When a force *F* acts on an area *A*, the pressure is *P*. What is the pressure when a force 2*F* acts on an area *A*/2?

A 4*P*   B 2*P*   C *P*   D ½*P*   E ¼*P*

37 A car's tyres are inflated so that an area of 50 cm² of each tyre is in contact with the ground. If the mass of the car is 1600 kg and it is evenly distributed between the four tyres, what is the pressure in each tyre?

    A 8 N/cm²   B 32 N/cm²   C 80 N/cm²   D 160 N/cm²   E 320 N/cm²

38 A spring has an unstretched length of 100 mm. When a force of 5 N is applied the new length of the spring is 150 mm. Assuming that the elastic limit is not exceeded, what is the length of the spring when a force of 7.5 N is applied?

    A 75 mm   B 125 mm   C 150 mm   D 175 mm   E 225 mm

39 When a mass of 300 g is hung on a spring, the length of the spring increases by 3.0 cm. By how much would it increase in length if a mass of 200 g were hung on it?

    A 2.0 cm   B 3.0 cm   C 4.0 cm   D 4.5 cm   E 6.0 cm

40 When viewed through a low-power microscope, smoke particles in an air cell are seen to be in continuous random motion. What causes this motion?

    A smoke particles colliding with smoke particles
    B air molecules colliding with smoke particles
    C air molecules colliding with air molecules
    D convection currents in the air
    E none of these

41 Which one of the following statements about the molecules of a substance is true?

    A In a liquid at a constant temperature they all have the same speed.
    B In a gas at a constant temperature a particular molecule has a fixed speed.
    C In a liquid they are very much further apart than in a solid.
    D In a solid the molecules will have more kinetic energy at a higher temperature.
    E When a liquid boils only those near the surface escape into the surroundings.

42 A bar of copper is heated from 10°C to 20°C. Which of the following statements is NOT true?

    A Its length will increase slightly.
    B Its electrical resistance will increase slightly.
    C Its density will increase slightly.
    D Its mass will remain unchanged.
    E Its weight will remain unchanged.

43 A fixed mass of gas has its pressure halved and its temperature, on the Kelvin scale, doubled. What is the ratio of the new volume to the original volume?

    A 1:4   B 1:2   C 1:1   D 2:1   E 4:1

44 A electric heating wire is immersed in 0.05 kg of oil in a calorimeter of negligible heat capacity. The temperature of the oil rises from 20°C to 50°C in 100 seconds. If the specific heat capacity of oil is 2000 J/kg°C, what is the power supplied by the heating coil?

    A 20 W   B 30 W   C 50 W   D 3000 W   E 3 000 000 W

45 How does heat travel through a vacuum?

    A by conduction only   D by conduction and convection
    B by convection only   E by conduction and radiation
    C by radiation only

46 In a ripple tank, waves travel a distance of 45 cm in 3 s. If the distance apart of the crests is 3 cm, what is the frequency of the vibrator causing the waves?

    A 5 Hz   B 7.5 Hz   C 11.25 Hz   D 20 Hz   E some other value

47 Which of the following describes the image formed in a pinhole camera by a distant upright object?

    A upright, real and magnified   D inverted, real and diminished
    B upright, real and diminished   E inverted, virtual and magnified
    C upright, virtual and diminished

48 Which of the following describes the image formed by a plane mirror?
   A   real and the same size as the object
   B   real and nearly the same size as the object
   C   virtual and the same size as the object
   D   virtual and nearly the same size as the object
   E   virtual and half the size of the object

49 What happens when waves move from deep to shallow water?
   A   Their wavelength decreases because their velocity decreases.
   B   Their wavelength decreases because their velocity increases.
   C   Their frequency increases because their velocity increases.
   D   Their frequency decreases because their velocity increases.
   E   Their frequency decreases because their velocity decreases.

50 Which one of the following must be moved in order to give the correct sequence of radiations in order of decreasing wavelength?
   A   radio waves   B ultraviolet rays   C infrared rays
   D   yellow light   E gamma rays

51 In what way are sound waves different from light waves?
   A   Sound waves need no medium, whereas light waves do.
   B   Sound waves need a medium, whereas light waves do not.
   C   Light waves travel through glass, whereas sound waves do not.
   D   Light waves are reflected, whereas sound waves are not.
   E   Sound waves are not refracted, whereas light waves are.

52 Which of the following statements about waves is true?
   A   Radio waves, light waves and sound waves will all travel through a vacuum.
   B   Radio waves and light waves will travel through a vacuum, sound waves will not.
   C   Sound waves will travel through a vacuum, radio waves and light waves will not.
   D   Light waves and sound waves will travel through a vacuum, radio waves will not.
   E   None of the waves will travel through a vacuum.

53 A loudspeaker gives out a note of frequency 100 Hz. If the speed of sound is 330 m/s, what is the wavelength of the sound?
   A 1.1 m   B 3.3 m   C 11 m   D 33 m   E 110 m

54 A rod of insulating material is given a positive charge by rubbing it with a piece of fabric. The fabric is then tested for electric charge. What would you expect the fabric to have?
   A   a positive charge equal to that on the rod
   B   a negative charge equal to that on the rod
   C   a positive charge less than that on the rod
   D   a negative charge greater than that on the rod
   E   no charge

Questions 55 and 56

Two coils of wire of resistance 2 ohms and 3 ohms, respectively, are connected in series with a 10 volt battery of negligible internal resistance as shown.

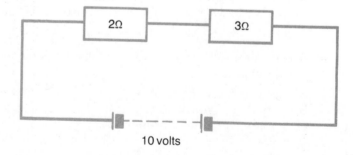

10 volts

55 What is the current through the 2 ohm coil?

    A 0.5 A   ·B 2 A   C 5 A   D 20 A   E 50 A

56 What is the potential difference across the 3 ohm coil?

    A 2 V   B 4 V   C 5 V   D 6 V   E 10 V

Questions 57 and 58

Similar cells, ammeters and resistors are used in the circuit shown. The cells and ammeters have negligible resistance. When one cell is connected in series with one ammeter and one resistor the ammeter reading is 0.1 A.

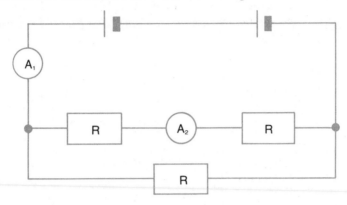

    A 0.1 A   B 0.2 A   C 0.3 A   D 0.4 A   E 0.5 A

57 Select from the list above the value of the current through ammeter A_1.

58 Select from the list above the value of the current through ammeter A_2.

59 A 24 W, 12 V headlamp is lit by connecting it to a 12 V battery of negligible resistance. What is the current through the headlamp?

    A 288 A   B 24 A   C 12 A   D 2 A   E 0.5 A

60 An electric fire is rated 250 V, 1000 W. If electricity costs 7p per unit what is the cost of running the fire for 5 hours?

    A 3.5p   B 7p   C 17.5p   D 35p   E 70p

61 Why is the outer casing of an electric iron generally connected to earth?

    A to prevent a serious electric shock   D to protect the iron

    B to complete the circuit   E to allow the current to get away

    C to prevent the fuse from burning out

62 A 12 V, 36 W lamp is connected across the output of a transformer. The output has 60 turns round the transformer. Which one of the following inputs to the transformer would enable the lamp to glow with normal brightness?

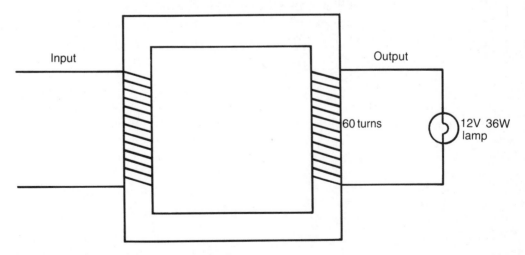

    A a voltage of 12 V d.c. and 36 turns on the input coil

    B a voltage of 120 V d.c. and 600 turns on the input coil

C a voltage of 12 V a.c. and 36 turns on the input coil
D a voltage of 120 V a.c. and 600 turns on the input coil
E a voltage of 120 V a.c. and 6 turns on the input coil

63 In a school experiment a stream of electrons passes through a horizontal slit and strikes an inclined screen so that a trace is seen as indicated in the diagram.

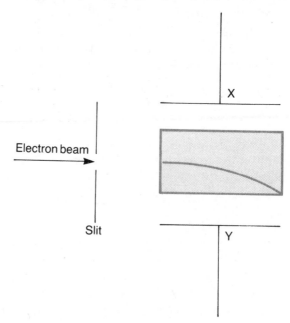

Which one of the following is the best explanation of the parabolic path?

A The electrons are falling under the influence of gravity.
B There is a magnetic field acting downwards between the plates.
C The electrons are slowing down and losing energy.
D Plate X has a positive potential relative to plate Y.
E Plate X has a negative potential with respect to plate Y.

64 Atoms of atomic number (proton number) 92 and mass number (nucleon number) 234 decay to form new atoms of atomic number 90 and mass number 230. What will the emissions consist of?

A electrons   D beta particles
B neutrons   E alpha particles
C gamma rays

65 Thorium 232 with atomic number 90 decays to element X by ejecting an alpha particle. Element X emits a beta particle to become element Y. Element Y emits another beta particle to become element Z. What are the mass number and the atomic number of element Z?

	Mass number	Atomic number
A	230	90
B	228	88
C	228	90
D	230	88
E	226	90

Answers to self-test questions

1 B	11 C	21 E	31 B	41 D	51 B	61 A
2 D	12 C	22 E	32 B	42 C	52 B	62 D
3 C	13 B	23 B	33 D	43 E	53 B	63 E
4 B	14 D	24 A	34 E	44 B	54 B	64 E
5 B	15 B	25 B	35 C	45 C	55 B	65 C
6 D	16 D	26 D	36 A	46 A	56 D	
7 C	17 C	27 A	37 C	47 D	57 C	
8 C	18 A	28 C	38 D	48 C	58 A	
9 D	19 C	29 D	39 A	49 A	59 D	
10 D	20 B	30 D	40 B	50 B	60 D	

Practice in answering examination questions

Multiple choice questions (answers p. 167)

1   You are the officer in charge of a spaceship travelling from our Galaxy to the Andromeda Galaxy. You are in deep space, the gravitational force due to surrounding galaxies is zero.
If your drive motors are off then you must be

     A   stationary
     B   decreasing in speed
     C   increasing in speed
     D   maintaining your present speed

2   An object with an initial speed of 3 m/s begins to accelerate at 2 m/s^2.
After 5 seconds its speed in m/s will be:

     A 2   B 3   C 10   D 13   E 15

(NICCEA Tier Q)

3   A body accelerates from rest at 4 m/s^2 for 5 s. What is its average speed?

     A 0.8 m/s   B 1.2 m/s   C 9 m/s   D 10 m/s   E 11 m/s

4   The mass of a moving object multiplied by its velocity is measuring the object's

     A   inertia   C   acceleration   E   energy
     B   weight   D   momentum

5   Which of the following is a unit of energy?

     A joule   B newton   C volt   D watt

(ULEAC B Paper 3F)

6   Which one of the following units could be used to measure the rate at which a machine is doing work?

     A   joule   C   newton metre   E   watt
     B   newton   D   newton per second

7   An object is dropped from a tower 50 m high. When it is 10 m from the ground what is the ratio of the object's potential energy to its kinetic energy?

     A 1:5   B 1:4   C 1:2   D 4:1   E 5:1

8

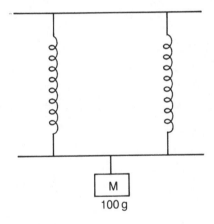

Force *F*

Pivot

— 6 m — — 9 m —

600N

A girl weighing 600 newtons sits 6 metres away from the pivot of a see-saw, as shown above. What force *F*, 9 metres away from the pivot, is needed to balance the see-saw?

A   300 newtons   C   450 newtons   E   900 newtons
B   400 newtons   D   600 newtons

9   A stone has a mass of 480 g and a volume of 160 cm^3. Its density is

A   76 800 g/cm^3 C   320 g/cm^3 E   0.3 g/cm^3
B   540 g/cm^3 D   3 g/cm^3

10   A car's tyres are inflated so that an area of 40 cm^2 of each is in contact with the ground. If the mass of the car is 1280 kg and is evenly distributed between the four tyres, what is the pressure exerted on the ground by each one? *g* = 10 N/kg

A   80 N/cm^2 C   200 N/cm^2 E   500 N/cm^2
B   160 N/cm^2 D   320 N/cm^2

Questions 11 and 12

Two springs are such that, when either is loaded with a mass of 200 g it stretches 4 cm. The masses of the springs may be ignored.

M
100 g

11   The springs are suspended in parallel and a load of 100 g is attached. What is the most likely stretch of each spring?

A 0.5 cm   B 1 cm   C 2 cm   D 4 cm   E 8 cm

12   The springs are suspended in series and a load of 200 g is attached. What is the total stretch of both springs together?

A 0.5 cm   B 1 cm   C 2 cm   D 4 cm   E 8 cm

13   Which of the following describes particles in a solid?

A   close together and stationary
B   close together and vibrating
C   close together and moving around at random
D   far apart and stationary
E   far apart and moving around at random

14   'Brownian motion' is the name for the movement of

A   a gas diffusing into a vacuum   D   molecules in a heated metal bar
B   electrons in an atom   E   smoke particles in air
C   ions in electrolysis

15 A gas is compressed and its temperature rises. Which one of the following happens to the molecules of the gas?

A They move closer together and have a greater average speed.
B They move closer together and their average speed is unchanged.
C They move closer together and have a smaller average speed.
D They remain at the same average distance apart and have a greater average speed.
E They remain at the same average distance apart and have a smaller average speed.

16 Each of the following blocks of metal has a mass of 1 kg and has 1000 J of energy supplied to it by an immersion heater. Which of the blocks shows the greatest temperature rise?

A iron (specific heat capacity 460 J/kg°C)
B copper (specific heat capacity 400 J/kg°C)
C brass (specific heat capacity 380 J/kg°C)
D lead (specific heat capacity 140 J/kg°C)
E aluminium (specific heat capacity 900 J/kg°C)

17 The graph shows the temperature change that takes place when a pure substance is cooled.

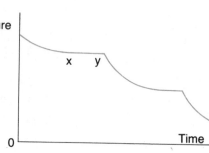

What change of state does the section X–Y of the graph represent?

A a solid to a gas
B a liquid to a solid
C a solid to a liquid
D a gas to a liquid
E a liquid to a gas

18 Two liquids are spilt on the hand. One is alcohol, the other is water, and both are at the same temperature. Why does the alcohol feel colder?

A It has a higher boiling point than water.
B It is a worse conductor of heat than water.
C It has a higher specific heat capacity than water.
D It evaporates more readily than water.
E It cools on evaporating.

19 When more molecules of a liquid return to it than escape from it, what is said to be happening?

A It is condensing.
B It is conducting.
C It is diffusing.
D It is evaporating.
E It is radiating.

20 Where does convection occur?

A only in solids
B only in liquids
C only in gases
D in solids and liquids
E in liquids and gases

21 Why does double glazing improve the heat insulation of houses?

A Glass of double thickness does not conduct heat.
B Radiation will not pass through two sheets of glass.
C The air trapped between the glass is a bad conductor of heat.

D   Convection currents between the glass sheets are restricted.
E   Radiation will not pass through the gap between the two sheets of glass.

Questions 22 and 23

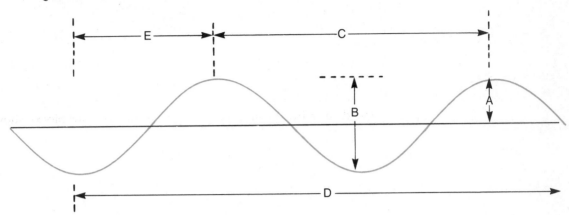

The diagram shows a wave. Which letter shows

22   the wavelength?

23   the amplitude?

24   Which of the following waves is not transverse?

A radio   B sound   C infrared   D light   E gamma rays

25   Which one of the following statements about the image produced in a pinhole camera is correct?

A   The image is bigger if the object is further away.
B   The image is smaller if the screen is nearer the pinhole.
C   The image is brighter if the object is further away.
D   The image is sharper if the pinhole is made bigger.
E   The image is bigger if the object is brighter.

26   When you look at yourself in a mirror you see an image of yourself. The image is

A   on the surface of the mirror.   D   caused by rays behind the mirror.
B   a real image behind the mirror.   E   a virtual image behind the mirror.
C   an inverted virtual image.

27   Which one of the following changes occurs when a light wave passes from air into glass?

A   Its wavelength increases.   D   Its frequency decreases.
B   Its speed decreases.   E   Its frequency increases.
C   Its speed increases.

28   An object O is placed 15 cm from a converging (convex) lens. The focal length of the lens is 5 cm.

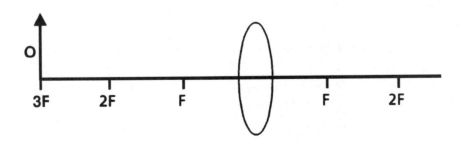

Which of the following lines correctly describes the type of image and where it is formed?

Type of image	Where formed
A virtual	between lens and F
B real	between lens and F
C virtual	beyond 2F
D virtual	between F and 2F
E real	between F and 2F

(NICCEA Tier Q)

29 Which of the following describes the image seen through a magnifying glass?

A It is real and upright.   D It is virtual and inverted.
B It is real and inverted.   E It is none of these.
C It is virtual and upright.

30 Which of the following describes the image formed on the retina of the human eye?

A It is magnified and erect.   D It is diminished and erect.
B It is diminished and inverted.   E It is magnified and inverted.
C It is life-size and virtual.

31 Light waves spread out when they pass through a very narrow gap. What is this effect called?

A refraction   D diffraction
B reflection   E dispersion
C interference

32 Which of the following examples of electromagnetic radiation has the shortest wavelength?

A radio waves   D visible light
B infrared rays   E X rays
C ultraviolet rays

33 Which of the following does NOT apply to sound waves?

A They transmit energy.
B They result from vibrations.
C They are propagated by a series of compressions and rarefactions.
D They travel fastest in a vacuum.
E They can be diffracted.

34 When a bat squeaks, the sound has a frequency of 30 000 Hz. The wavelength of the sound is 0.01 m.
The speed of the sound wave is

A 30 000 m/s
B 3000 m/s
C 300 m/s
D 30 m/s

(ULEAC B Paper 3H)

35 Which one of the following is true for the resistance of a voltmeter and the way in which it is normally connected to a circuit?

Resistance	Connection
A zero	parallel
B low	series
C low	parallel
D high	series
E high	parallel

36 What is the most probable value of the current flowing through a 12 V, 24 W car headlamp when operating on a 6 V supply?

A 0.2 A   B 1 A   C 1.2 A   D 2 A   E 4 A

37 Fuses are available which melt when the current through them exceeds 2, 5, 10, 15 or 30 A. Which one of these would be the most suitable for a circuit in which an electric fire rated at 2.5 kW is to be connected, if the supply voltage is 240 V?

A 2 A fuse   B 5 A fuse   C 10 A fuse   D 15 A fuse   E 30 A fuse

38 An electric lamp converts 200 joules in 5 seconds
The power of the lamp is

A 5 W   B 40 W   C 200 W   D 1000 W

(ULEAC B Paper 31)

39 The diagram shows the strength of an electromagnet with a fixed number of turns of wire as a function of the steady current passing through the turns.
Why can the strength of the electromagnet not be increased above the value of the line *PQ*?

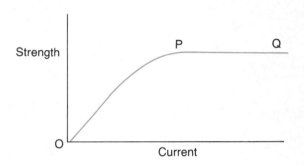

A   The turns of wire get too hot.
B   The current through the turns cannot be increased further.
C   The small magnets (domains) within the core have all been aligned by point *P*.
D   The core gets too hot.
E   The core is made of a material which is unsuitable for use in an electromagnet.

40 Which of the following changes would not affect the direction of the force on a wire carrying a current in a magnetic field?

A   The direction of the magnetic field is reversed.
B   The magnetic field is removed.
C   The direction of the current is reversed.
D   The current is switched off.
E   Both the direction of the magnetic field and the direction of the current are reversed.

41 The diagram shows a current flowing through a wire placed in a magnetic field. The strength of the force acting on the wire is *F*.

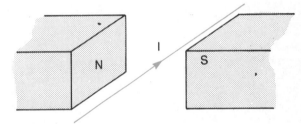

The current flowing through the wire is now halved and the strength of the magnetic field is doubled. Which one of the following statements is true about the force now acting on the wire?

A   It has strength 4*F* and is vertical.
B   It has strength 4*F* and is horizontal.
C   It has strength 2*F* and is horizontal.
D   It has strength *F* and is vertical.
E   It has strength *F* and is horizontal.

42 When the bar magnet is moved into the coil the meter is deflected.

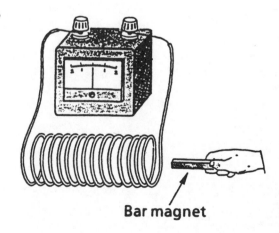

Bar magnet

The meter will deflect in the OPPOSITE direction when:

A   the magnet is pulled out of the coil;
B   the coil is moved towards the magnet;
C   the magnet is held at rest inside the coil;
D   the magnet is moved more quickly into the coil;
E   the magnet is moved more slowly into the coil.

(NICCEA Tier Q)

43 For which of the following is an alternating current essential in its operation?

A   an electromagnet   C   a galvanometer   E   an electric fire
B   a transformer   D   an electric lamp

44 A step-down transformer has a turns ratio of 6:1. A 240 V alternating current supply at a frequency of 50 Hz is connected to the primary coil. What is the frequency of the alternating current output?

A   0.2 Hz   B   5 Hz   C   10 Hz   D   50 Hz   E   500 Hz

45 What is a particle with a mass of 1 atomic mass unit and a charge of +1 called?

A   an electron   C   a positron   E   an alpha particle
B   a gamma particle   D   a proton

46 Which one of the following quantities in an atom represents the mass number of the atom?

A   the number of protons plus the number of neutrons
B   the number of protons plus the number of electrons
C   the number of electrons
D   the number of protons
E   the number of neutrons

47 When two plates on the Earth's surface move against each other the result is likely to be

A   earthquake
B   fog
C   high tide
D   snowstorm

(ULEAC B Paper 3H)

48 A seismometer is used to detect

A   air pressure above cloud level.
B   movements of the Earth's surface.
C   radioactive background count.
D   ultrasound.

(ULEAC B Paper 3H)

49 In one year

A   the Earth orbits the Sun once.
B   the Moon orbits the Earth once.
C   the Earth turns once about its axis.
D   Venus orbits the Sun once.

(ULEAC B Paper 3F)

50 The nearest star to the Earth is

A   Rigel   B   Venus   C   Sirius   D   the Sun

(ULEAC B Paper 3F)

51 The sketch shows the masses and positions of two moons relative to planet X.

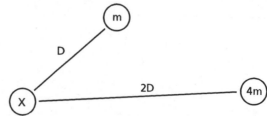

The gravitational force between $4m$ and X is F_1. Between m and X it is F_2 where
A $F_1 = F_2$ B $F_1 = 2F_2$ C $F_2 = 2F_1$ D $F_2 = 4F_1$

(ULEAC B Paper 3H)

Answers to multiple choice questions

1 D	11 B	21 C	31 D	41 D	51 A
2 D	12 E	22 C	32 E	42 A	
3 D	13 B	23 A	33 D	43 B	
4 D	14 E	24 B	34 C	44 D	
5 A	15 A	25 B	35 E	45 D	
6 E	16 D	26 E	36 C	46 A	
7 B	17 D	27 B	37 D	47 A	
8 B	18 D	28 E	38 B	48 B	
9 D	19 A	29 C	39 C	49 A	
10 A	20 E	30 B	40 E	50 D	

Questions requiring short or structured answers (answers p. 203)

Questions of the short answer or structured type are used most by the Examining Groups. The answer can be a single word, or number, a phrase, or a few sentences. You should read about tackling these sorts of questions on p. 11 before starting.

Chapter 2

1 (a) A bus starts from rest at O on a level road and climbs a hill ABCD which then levels out again at DE as shown in Figure 1. The bus then slows down and stops at a bus stop at E.

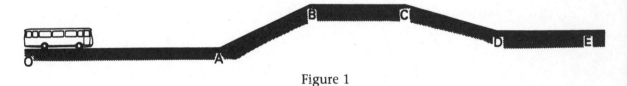

Figure 1

A velocity–time graph is drawn below in Figure 2, to show the motion of the bus.

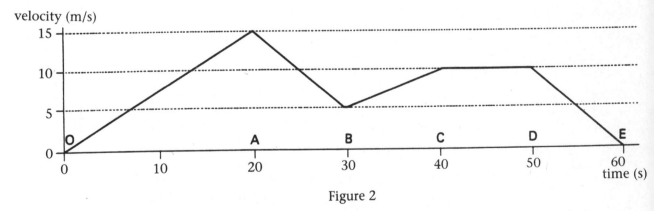

Figure 2

In which regions OA, AB, BC, CD, DE is the bus:
   (i)   accelerating?
   (ii) decelerating?
   (iii) travelling with uniform velocity?
         Give the value of this uniform velocity.   (6)

(b) At which point, other than O, is the bus at rest? (1)

(c) Using information from the graph:
  (i) State a region where the bus is accelerating.
     Calculate this acceleration.
  (ii) State a region where the bus is decelerating.
     Calculate this deceleration.
  (iii) Calculate the distance travelled in the region AB. (8)

(d) Figure 3 shows a displacement time graph for the bus as it starts up again from the bus stop at E.

displacement (m)

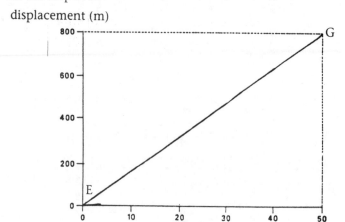

Figure 3

Using the graph:
  (i) What does the graph tell us about the speed of the bus?
  (ii) Calculate the speed of the bus. (4)

(NEAB Option Q)

2   The diagram below is the graph of a journey made by a train. Its speed is measured in metres per second (m/s) and time is measured in seconds (s).

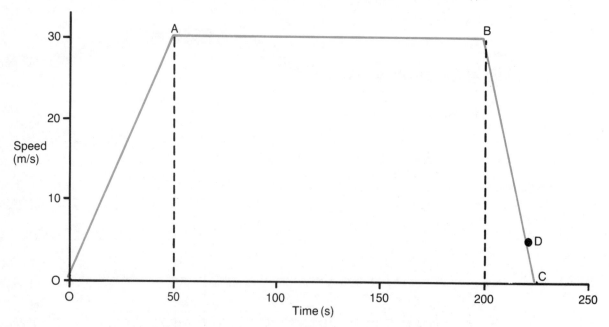

(a) What is the greatest speed reached by the train?
(b) How is the train moving on the section represented by the line AB?
(c) How is the train moving on the section represented by the line BC?
(d) Which of the points O, A, B or C represents the stage at which the brakes are first applied?
(e) The line BC is steeper than the line OA. What does this tell you about the rates at which the train speeds up and slows down?
(f) Calculate how far the train travelled between the stages in its journey represented by the points O and A.

3   A child steps out into the path of an oncoming car. The graph shows how the speed of the car changes from the moment the driver sees the child until the car stops.

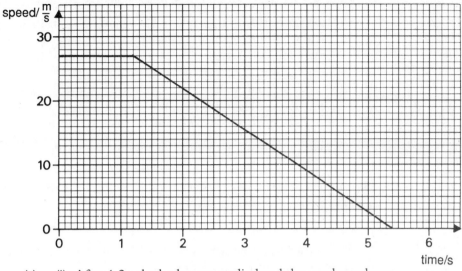

(a)   (i)   After 1.2 s the brakes are applied and the car slows down. Calculate the value of the deceleration (negative acceleration) of the car while the brakes are applied.   (3)
      (ii) Calculate the distance travelled by the car from the moment the driver first saw the child.   (3)

(b) The sequence of the diagrams below shows what can happen to the occupants of a car when it brakes hard.

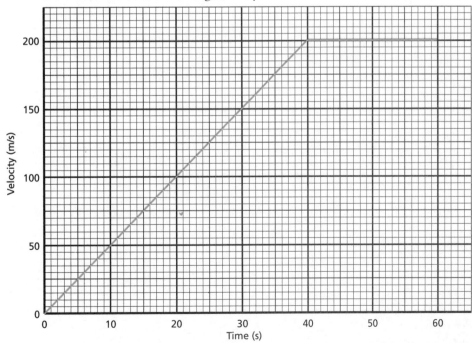

Explain carefully why the child who is standing in the back of the car should wear a seat belt.   (4)

(MEG Further Tier)

4   (a) The graph shows how the velocity of an aeroplane changes with time as it takes off until it reaches its cruising velocity.

If it is airborne after 25 seconds, calculate

    (i) the distance travelled along the runway before becoming airborne, (3)
    (ii) the acceleration of the plane along the runway. (3)

(b) When the plane crosses the coast a piece of ice falls from the wing. The plane is at a height of 10 km and travelling at its cruising velocity. Ignoring air resistance and taking the acceleration of free fall as 10 m/s² calculate

    (i) the time taken for the ice to hit the ground,
    (ii) the distance from the coast that ice hits the ground,
    (iii) the vertical velocity of the ice as it hits the ground,
    (iv) the horizontal velocity of the ice as it hits the ground. (14)

(c) Sketch the path of the ice as it falls from the plane. (4)

(NEAB Option R)

5 An object is released from a helicopter which is hovering (stationary) 180 m above the ground. Ignore the effect of air resistance.

(a) Calculate how long it takes the object to reach the ground.

The helicopter now starts to move horizontally at a speed of 40 m/s, and drops a second object from a height of 180 m.

(b) How long does it take the second object to reach the ground?

(c) Calculate the horizontal distance travelled by the second object between leaving the helicopter and reaching the ground.

Chapter 3

6 The diagram shows emergency food supplies falling with a parachute attached. The arrows show forces acting on the food supplies and the parachute.

(a) Give the name of each force for force A and force B. (2)

(b) The food supplies are falling with a maximum speed.

    (i) What do we call this speed?
    (ii) What can you say about the forces acting on the food supplies at this time? (2)

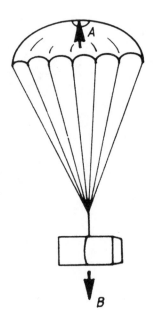

(c) The graph on the next page shows how the speed of the food supplies changed as they fell from the delivery plane.

    (i) When did the parachute open?
    (ii) What was the fastest speed reached by the food supplies?
    (iii) How far did the supplies fall between times D and E? (4)

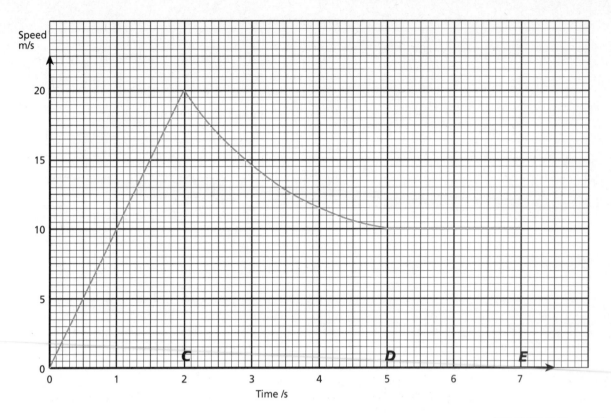

(ULEAC B Paper 2I)

7   An instrument used by an astronaut has a mass of 25 kg on the Earth.
    The gravitational field strength on the Earth is 10 N/kg and on the Moon it is 1.7 N/kg.

   (a) What would be the mass of the instrument on the Moon?
   (b) What would be the weight of the instrument on the Moon?

8   (a) In each of the following situations name the force which keeps the object moving in a circular path (i.e. say what provides the centripetal force).

      (i) The Moon moving round the Earth.
      (ii) A mass swung in a horizontal circle on the end of a string.
      (iii) A car moving round a corner.

   (b) In what direction does the centripetal force always act?

9   The idea of conservation of momentum is useful when considering rocket propulsion and collisions.

   (a) A space rocket carries its fuel with it as well as oxygen The fuel, such as hydrogen, reacts explosively with oxygen, producing steam, which is forced out of the rocket at high speed.

(i) Explain what is meant by 'the conservation of momentum' and explain how this applies to the space rocket. (3)

(ii) To increase its velocity a space rocket uses a total of 10 kg of hydrogen and oxygen producing steam moving at 10 000 m/s. If the mass of the space rocket is 25 000 kg, calculate its increase in velocity. (3)

(b) The diagram below shows a collision just about to happen.

The speed limit on the road is 25 metres per second. The vehicles crash head-on and instantly stop. Fortunately nobody is seriously hurt. The police know that the van (mass 2 100 kg) was travelling at a speed of 15 m/s from the tachometer reading. They have to calculate the speed of the car (mass 900 kg).

(i) Calculate the momentum of the van just before the collision. (2)

(ii) Explain how the police can use the conservation of momentum to show that the car must have been speeding. Make sure that you calculate and record the speed of the car. (4)

(SEG Higher Tier)

10 A girl of mass 45 kg jumps horizontally out of a small boat, with a velocity of 2 m/s. The mass of the boat is 15 kg. What is the change in the speed of the boat as the girl jumps out, and in what direction?

11 A 2 g bullet travelling at 100 m/s embeds itself in a stationary block of wood of mass 998 g which is at rest but free to move. What is the velocity of the block of wood as it starts to move?

12 (a) A car of mass 1200 kg is being towed at a constant speed of 5 m/s by a breakdown lorry. The force of friction on the car at this speed is 400 N.

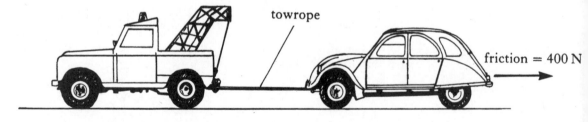

towrope

friction = 400 N

What size of force is exerted by the tow-rope on the car? (1)

(b) The force exerted by the tow-rope on the car is increased to 2000 N. Assuming that the force of friction on the car remains constant at 400 N, find the acceleration of the car. (3)

(SEB Standard Grade Credit Level)

13 A ball of mass 0.2 kg is thrown vertically upwards from ground level and reaches a maximum height of 3.2 m. Ignoring air resistance calculate

(a) The potential energy the ball has gained when it is 3.2 m above the ground.
(b) The kinetic energy the ball gains in falling to the ground.
(c) The speed of the ball just before it reaches the ground.
(d) The acceleration of the ball as it is falling.
(e) The force acting on the ball as it is falling.

14 The diagram shows the overall stopping distance needed for a car travelling in a straight line at 20 m/s.

16 m — **Thinking distance**   38 m — **Braking distance**

The thinking distance is the distance travelled by the car in the time it takes the driver to react and put on the brakes (reaction time).

(a) Calculate the reaction time of the driver. (1)

(b) The mass of the car is 1140 kg.
    (i) Calculate the kinetic energy of the car when it is travelling at 20 m/s.
    (ii) What is the work done in stopping the car?
    (iii) Calculate the average braking force needed to stop the car in a distance of 38 m.
    (iv) Describe what has happened to the kinetic energy of the car when it has stopped. (6)

(c) The diagram shows a car travelling at a constant speed round a right-hand bend.

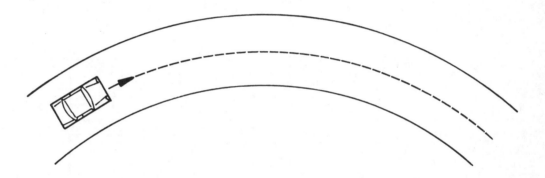

Passengers in the car would feel as though they were being forced outwards as the car went round the bend.
Explain why they would feel this force, and describe fully what is really happening to them. (4)

(d) Car makers build into their cars a number of safety features. One of these is a crumple zone. The crumple zones are designed to collapse in a serious collision. These are shown in the diagram. Explain clearly in terms of momentum the physics behind this safety feature. (4)

Crumple zone   Crumple zone

(ULEAC A Paper 2H)

15 The sketch shows a gymnast on a trampoline. She reaches a height of 5 m above the trampoline.

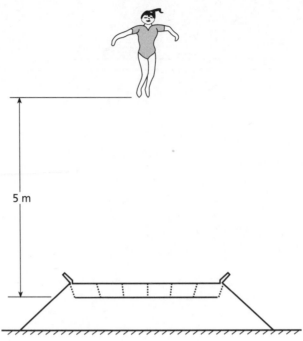

5 m

The graph below shows how the speed of the gymnast changes as she exercises on the trampoline.

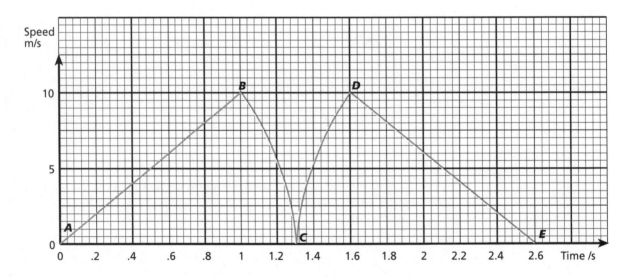

(a) Describe in words what is happening to the gymnast between points
    (i) A and B
    (ii) B and C   (4)

(b) In the sketch the gymnast is shown with maximum gravitational potential energy.
    (i) Which place on the graph shows the speed of the gymnast at this point?
    (ii) Describe the energy changes which occur during the periods
        1. B to C
        2. C to D
        3. D to E   (7)

(c) (i) The mass of the gymnast is 60 kg. Use the graph above to calculate the maximum value of the kinetic energy of the gymnast.
    (ii) How does your answer compare with the maximum potential energy of the gymnast?   (5)

(ULEAC B Paper 2H)

16 As a rocket moves from the Earth towards the Moon it does work against the Earth's gravitational field.

      (i) What is happening to the gravitational potential energy of the rocket as it moves from the Earth to the Moon?

      (ii) Explain why less fuel is needed to return the rocket from the Moon to the Earth than to send the rocket from the Earth to the Moon.

      (iii) Astronauts in orbit around the Moon experience 'weightlessness'. Explain why this is so.

        (7)

(ULEAC A Paper 2I)

17 An electric motor is used to lift a mass of 1 kg through a height of 3.2 m at a constant speed in a time of 8 s.

(a) Calculate

      (i) the potential energy gained by the mass.

      (ii) the useful work done by the motor.

      (iii) the useful power output of the motor.

(b) When the mass reaches 2.45 m above the floor the string breaks.

      (i) How much kinetic energy does the mass gain in falling to the floor?

      (ii) What is the speed of the mass just before it reaches the floor?

18 The diagram shows the forces acting on a car as it travels along a level road.

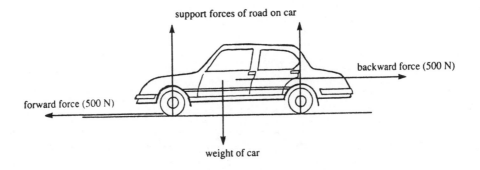

The backward force opposing its motion is 500 N.
The forward force exerted on the car is 500 N.

(a) The speed of the car is 25 m/s. Calculate the work done by the forward force of 500 N in 20 seconds

      (4)

(b) The petrol supplies 1000 kJ of energy to the engine in 20 seconds. Calculate the efficiency of the engine.

      (2)

(MEG Central Tier)

19 (a) The pie chart shows the five sources of energy used by a country.

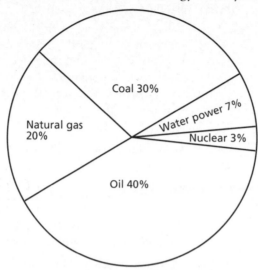

The table shows the proportional use and estimated reserves of coal, oil and natural gas.

	Relative estimated reserves	*Relative quantity used/year*
Coal	500	1.25
Oil	100	3
Natural Gas	90	1.5

(i) Explain why it is always difficult to make accurate predictions of how long reserves will last. (4)

(ii) Why will the pie chart be likely to be different in about 20 years time? (2)

(iii) Explain the economic, environmental and social **benefits** of using nuclear energy as the main source of providing electrical power. (4)

(b) Pumped storage power stations are used to produce electricity during periods of peak demand. Water is stored in one reservoir and allowed to flow through a pipe to another reservoir at a lower level. The falling water is used to turn turbines which are linked to generators.

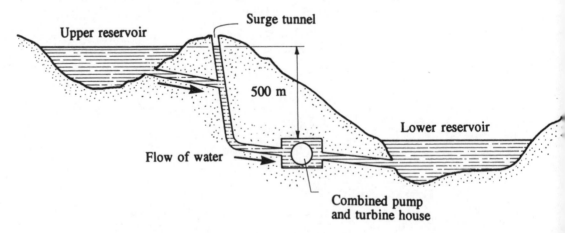

In one such power station 400 kg of water passes through the turbines every second after falling 500 m. The gravitational field strength is 10 N/kg. Assume that no energy is wasted.

(i) What is the weight of 400 kg of water? (2)

(ii) Calculate the decrease in gravitational energy when 400 kg of water falls 500 m. (2)

(iii) What is the power delivered to the turbines by this falling water? (2)

(iv) If the generator is perfectly efficient calculate the current it produces if the output voltage is 20 000 V. (3)

(v) Why are pumped storage power stations used to produce electricity for a few hours and not for continuous generation of electricity? (2)

(SEG Higher Tier)

20 (a) Explain the difference between a vector and a scalar quantity.

(b) Give two examples each of vector and scalar quantities.

21 The diagram shows four spring balances, all pulling on a knot at P. The strings are at 90° to each other.

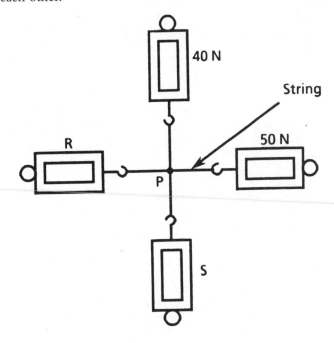

P is at rest. The readings on two of the spring balances are shown on the diagram. What are the readings on the spring balances R and S? (2)

(NICCEA Tier Q)

Chapter 4

22 The diagram below shows a uniform METRE RULE of weight 2 N. The rule is pivoted 20 cm from one end and a force F keeps it balanced.

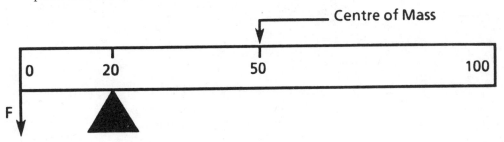

What is the value of the force F? (2)

(NICCEA Tier Q)

23 The diagram below shows a uniform rod pivoted through its centre. A spring balance is attached to the rod 15 cm from the pivot. A force of 7.5 N is acting 40 cm from the pivot. The rod is balanced, and its weight may be neglected.

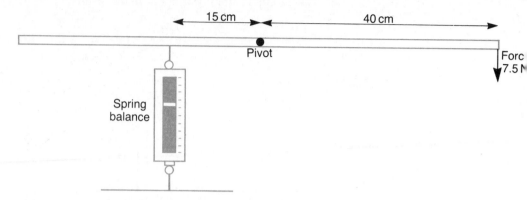

(a) Calculate the reading of the spring balance.
(b) State the value and direction of the force that the pivot exerts on the rod.

24 The diagram shows a lever being used to lift the lid from a tin of paint.

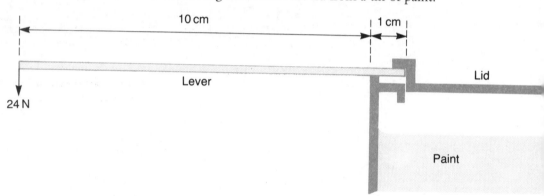

(a) On the diagram
    (i) mark the position of the pivot *P*.
    (ii) draw an arrow to show the direction of the force *F*, which the lever exerts on the lid.

(b) Calculate the moment of the force of 24 N about the pivot.
(c) Calculate the value of the force *F* which the lever exerts on the lid.
(d) What is the value of the force that the lever exerts on the pivot?
(e) If the force *F* is too small to lift the lid, suggest two changes which you might make to increase the value of *F*.

Chapter 5

25 (a) Calculate the surface area of a cube of side 2 cm.
    (b) Calculate the volume of the same cube.
    (c) Find its mass if it has a density of 8 g/cm^3.

Chapter 6

26 A hovercraft has a mass of 10 000 kg. It hovers at a constant height above the ground.

(a) Calculate the weight of the hovercraft.
(b) What is the value of the upward force exerted by the air cushion?
(c) The hovercraft has a rectangular shape of length 20 m and width 5 m. Calculate the pressure excess (above atmosphere) of the air in the cushion under the craft.
(d) The hovercraft accelerates horizontally at 2.5 m/s^2. Calculate the horizontal force exerted by the driving propeller. You may ignore air resistance.

27 The diagram shows part of the hydraulic braking system of a motor car.

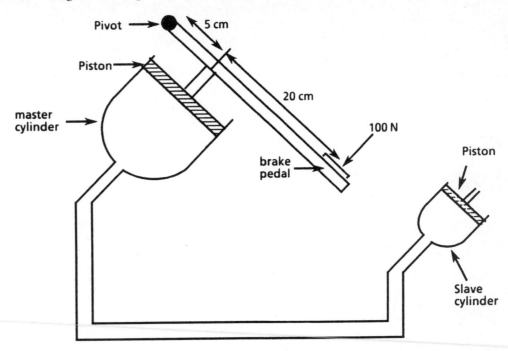

(i) Mark with an arrow on the diagram, the direction in which the piston in the slave cylinder moves when the driver presses down on the brake pedal. (1)

(ii) Explain why the downward force on the brake pedal causes the piston in the slave cylinder to move. (1)

(iii) The driver pushes down on the brake pedal with a force of 100 N. Calculate the force that this causes on the piston in the master cylinder. Show clearly how you obtain your answer. (3)

(iv) Find the pressure in Pascals in the brake fluid when the force on the master cylinder piston is 300 N. Show clearly how you obtain your answer. The master cylinder piston has an area of 20 cm^2. (3)

(v) The piston in the master cylinder has an area 10 times that of the piston in the slave cylinder. What is the force on the slave cylinder piston when the force on the master cylinder piston is 300 N? Show clearly how you obtain your answer. (2)

(NICCEA Tier R)

Chapter 8

28 (a) A spring has a spring constant of 5 N/cm. What force is needed to extend it by 6 cm? (3)

(b) Give another unit that could be used to measure spring constant. (1)

(c) A block of expanded polystyrene has a mass of 20 g and a volume of 500 cm^3. Calculate its density. (3)

(MEG Nuffield Central Tier)

29 The model shown in the diagram is sometimes used to represent the arrangement of molecules in a solid.

(a) What do the springs represent?

(b) How may the model be used to show what happens when a solid is heated?

(c) State how the movement of molecules in a liquid differs from the movement of molecules in a solid.

(d) Why is energy needed to melt a solid into a liquid at the same temperature?

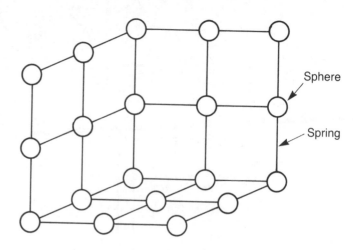

Sphere

Spring

Chapter 9

30 (a) Explain in terms of the kinetic theory why a metal bar expands on heating.

(b) Two metal plates may be riveted together by placing a white hot rivet in the hole through the two plates. The head of the rivet is then hammered flat. Explain why the plates are held more tightly together when the rivet has cooled.

(c) A bimetallic strip is made by riveting together a strip of iron and a strip of brass so that they cannot move separately. When heated, brass expands more than iron. Draw a diagram to show the shape of the bimetallic strip after it has been heated. Label the metals.

31 The photograph shows an expansion gap in a road.

(a) (i) Why is the gap needed?
(ii) What would happen if there were no expansion gap? (3)

(b) What would happen to the size of the gap:
(i) on a hot day,
(ii) on a cold day? (2)

(c) A mercury thermometer is used to measure temperature. On a hot day the mercury level rises. What happens to each of the following on a hot day?
(i) the **volume** of mercury in the thermometer
(ii) the **mass** of mercury in the thermometer
(iii) the **average speed** of the molecules in the mercury
(iv) the **number** of mercury molecules in the thermometer (4)

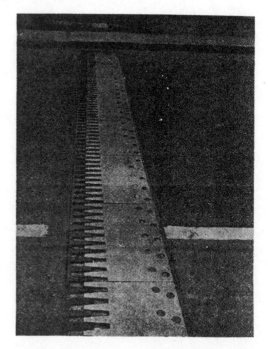

(ULEAC B Paper 2I)

Chapter 10

32 Boyle's Law applies to a fixed mass of many gases kept at a constant temperature. The Law states that the pressure (p) of the gas is inversely proportional to its volume (V). In symbols this may be written $p \propto 1/V$.

In an experiment with oxygen at a temperature of 300 K, several pairs of values of p and V were measured. The values of p were then plotted against values of $1/V$.

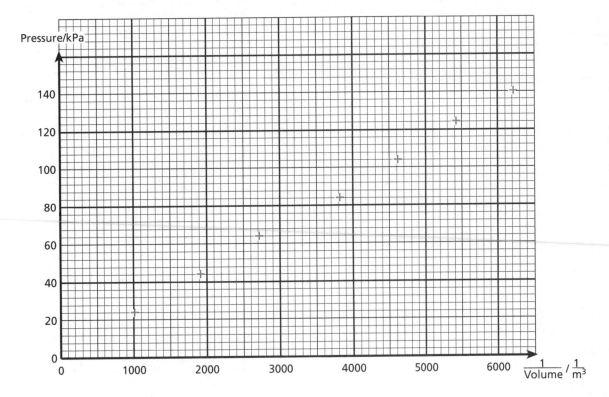

(a) Explain how the results show that Boyle's Law applies to oxygen. (2)

(b) Explain whether or not the experiment shows that the Law applies to oxygen at all pressures. (2)

(c) What was the volume of oxygen in the experiment when the pressure was 76 kPa? (3)

(d) (i) Draw on the graph the line that will be obtained if the experiment is repeated at a temperature of 600 K for the same range of pressures. (2)

   (ii) What assumptions have you made in drawing this line? (2)

(MEG Central Tier)

33 Some air at a pressure of 1 atmosphere and a temperature of 27°C occupies a volume of 1 litre.

(a) The air is heated to 177°C at constant pressure. What will be its new volume?

(b) The air is now cooled to its original temperature keeping the volume constant. Calculate its final pressure.

Chapter 11

34 When 1 kg of water was heated for 5 minutes with an immersion heater the water's temperature rose by 30°C.

To the questions that follow answer **either**; greater than 30°C; **or** less than 30°C; **or** equal to 30°C.

What would be the temperature rise if the same heater heated

   (i) 2 kg of water for 9 minutes?

   (ii) 1 kg of paraffin for 5 minutes (given that the specific heat capacity of paraffin is less than that of water)? (2)

Chapter 12

35 Complete the following sentences:
  (a) Heat travels by....................in solids.
  (b) Heat travels mainly by .... in liquids and gases.
  (c) Heat travels mainly by .... in space.

36 (a) The diagram shows a simple way of investigating which materials are the best conductors of heat.

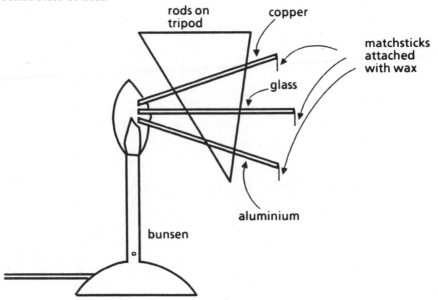

To make the test fair all the rods are placed at the same time in roughly the same place in the bunsen flame.
Give two other precautions, relating to the rods, you would need to take to ensure the test was fair. (2)
Why do the matchsticks eventually fall from the rods? (1)
Which rod would drop its matchstick first? Explain your answer. (2)

  (b) The diagram shows the hot-water supply system often found in a house.

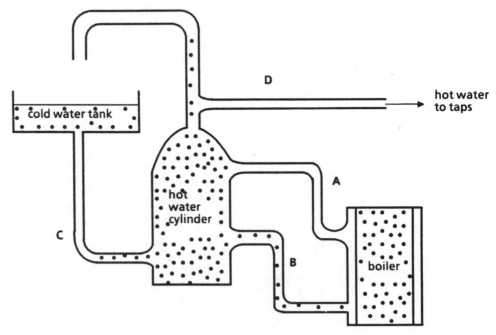

Mark clearly with arrows on the diagram the direction in which the water flows in pipes A, B and C. (3)
What name is given to the movement of water in this way? (1)
Explain why it is important that pipes A and D are lagged with an insulating material like fibreglass. (1)

(c) Heat can escape from your home through the roof, walls and chimney and through other routes.

Write down ONE of these other routes for heat to escape from your home. How could the amount of heat lost through this route be reduced? (2)

(NICCEA Tier Q)

37 (a) To compare the rate at which two different types of surface absorb radiant heat, the apparatus shown below was set up.
Can X has a polished surface and can Y has a dull black surface.
The starting temperature of the water in each can was 20°C.

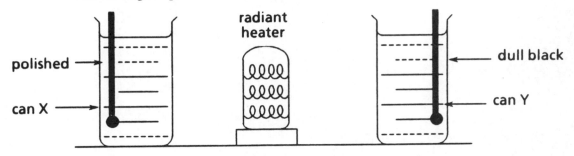

(i) To make this a fair comparison state TWO things that should be the same for each can. (1)
(ii) Which can will show the greater rise in temperature? Explain your answer. (2)

(b) The loss of heat from a house can take place through the roof, through the floor and through the walls. For each of these ways suggest how the heat loss can be reduced. In each case name the method of heat transfer that is being reduced. (3)

(NICCEA Tier R)

Chapter 13

38 (a) Waves may be either transverse or longitudinal. Why are longitudinal waves so named?
(b) Which of the following are transverse waves and which are longitudinal?
Waves on water, sound waves, radio waves, light waves.

39 A cork is floating in water. A stone is dropped into the water.

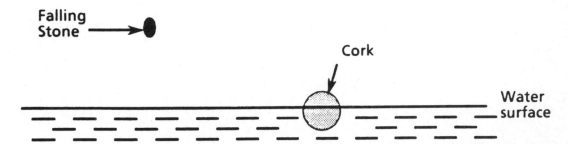

(i) After a short time the cork begins to move. Describe how the cork moves. (1)

(ii) What property of a wave causes the cork to move? (1)

The graph below shows how the displacement of the cork from its original position varies with time.

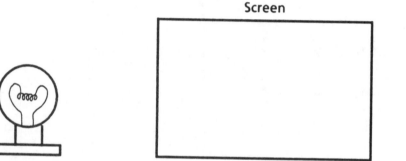

(iii) What is the amplitude and frequency of the water wave? (3)

(iv) The water waves have a wavelength of 0.8 m. Calculate the velocity of the water waves. Show clearly how you obtain your answer. (3)

(NICCEA Tier R)

Chapter 14

40 A pinhole camera is used to view the image of a filament bulb.

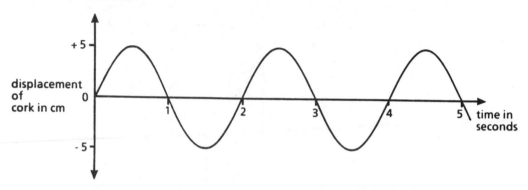

Screen

(a) What happens to the image as the bulb is moved further **away** from the pinhole? (1)

(b) Draw a sketch of how the filament of the bulb appears on the screen of the pinhole camera. (1)

(NICCEA Tier Q)

41 The diagram shows a periscope which may be used to see behind when towing a caravan. Only one mirror has been drawn in.

(a) Draw the second mirror in the correct position.

(b) Draw a ray of light from the top of the object to the eye.

(c) Draw a ray of light from the bottom of the object to the eye.

(d) What is the main disadvantage of this type of periscope?

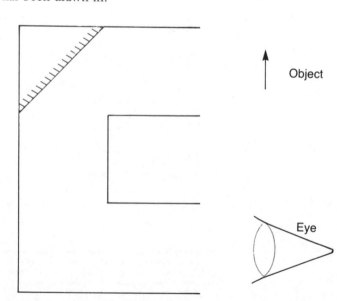

Object

Eye

Chapter 15

42 The diagram shows three rays of light from one point on the bottom of a swimming-bath reaching the surface.

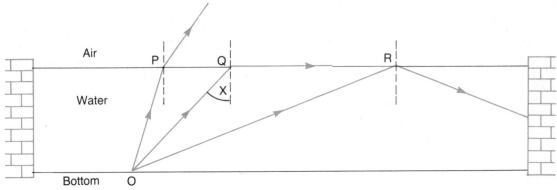

(a) What name is given to
  (i) the bending of the ray at P,
  (ii) the angle of incidence marked X?

(b) Explain why the ray bends in the direction shown at
  (i) the point P,
  (ii) the point R.

43 (a) Use some of the words in the box to name the parts of the eye.

| cornea | lens | nerve | pupil | retina |

(3)

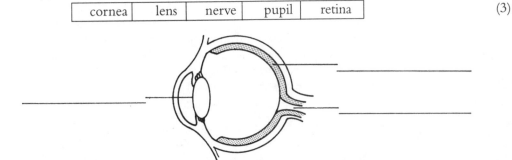

(b) Use the words in the box to complete the sentences which follow

| iris | lens | optic nerve | pupil | retina |

  (i) The light goes into the eye through the.......................... .
  (ii) The .... controls the amount of light getting into the eye.
  (iii) The .... focuses the light.
  (iv) An image forms on the ....
  (v) The .... carries the message to the brain.

(5)

(c) The diagram shows a common sight defect.

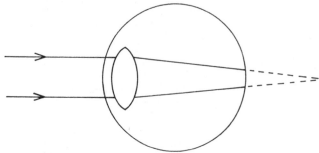

  (i) Name this defect.
  (ii) In front of the eye, draw a lens which will correct this defect.

(2)

(ULEAC B Paper 2I)

44 Fill in the blank spaces with the correct word(s) in the following passage.
A person suffers from long sight because his eye lens is too .... When looking
at a close object the image is brought to focus ....the retina. This fault may
be remedied by using spectacles with a .... lens so that the image is now
formed .... the retina.

45 Fill in the blank spaces with the correct word(s) in the following passage.
A person suffers from short sight because his eyeball is too .... When
looking at a distant object the image is brought to focus .... the retina. This
fault may be remedied by using spectacles with a .... lens so that the image
is now formed .... the retina.

Chapter 16

46 The diagram shows the diffraction of light waves passing through a narrow slit.

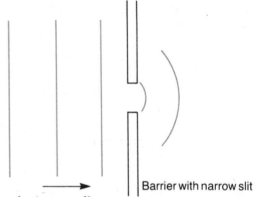

Barrier with narrow slit

(a) How could the spreading of the waves be increased?
(b) Does the wavelength of the light increase, decrease or remain the same as the
light passes through the slit?
(c) What change, if any, would you notice in the diffraction caused by the slit, if the
wavelength of the incoming light were greater?

47 To observe Young's fringes a blackened microscope slide with two slits close
together is placed between a lamp and a screen, in a dark room, as shown in the
diagram. Bright and dark bands (fringes) are seen on the screen.

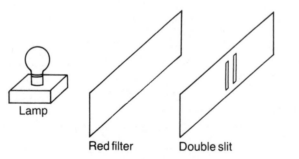
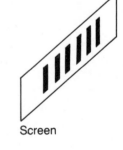

Lamp

Red filter   Double slit   Screen

(a) What property of light does this experiment demonstrate?
(b) (i) If light from the two slits arrives at the screen 'in step', do bright or dark
bands appear?
(ii) If the light reaches the screen 'out of step', what sort of bands appear on
the screen?
The pattern on the screen can be explained by considering the difference in path
length as shown below.

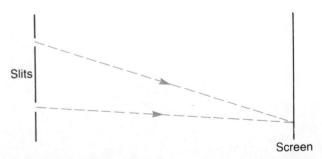

Slits

Screen

(c) What type of band will be seen on the screen in each of the following cases?
  (i) The paths are equal in length.
  (ii) The paths are different by one wavelength.
  (iii) The paths are different by half a wavelength.

(d) Blue light has a shorter wavelength than red light. What would happen to the fringe separation if a blue filter were used instead of a red one?

(e) What would happen to the fringe separation if the slits were replaced by two slits which were closer together?

48 The map shows part of the South coast of England with two radio navigation beacons P and Q, 80 km apart. Both transmit waves in step with one another. The waves have the same amplitude and a constant frequency of 1200 kHz. A ship is at a point X exactly midway between the two beacons.

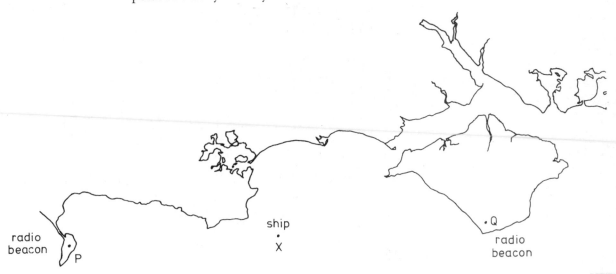

(a) Calculate the number of wavelengths of the radio waves which equals the distance between beacon P and point X. The speed of radio waves is 3×10^8 m/s. (4)

(b) Explain why the ship detects a radio wave which has twice the amplitude of the wave emitted by each beacon. (2)

(c) The ship moves 62.5 m nearer the beacon Q. Explain why the radio waves from P and Q are out of step when they reach the ship. (2)

(d) What is the amplitude of the radio wave detected by the ship in this position? Explain your answer. (1)

(e) Radio waves are at one end of the electromagnetic spectrum and light waves are in the middle. Choose one other type of electromagnetic wave and
  (i) state its approximate position in the electromagnetic spectrum,
  (ii) state one use of the wave,
  (iii) and explain why it is suitable for this use. (3)

(f) Radio waves can be *polarized*. Explain what this means. You may find it helpful to draw a diagram. (2)

(MEG Further Tier)

Chapter 17

49 A ship fires a gun and the crew hear an echo from the cliff face opposite 5 s later. If the velocity of sound is 300 m/s, what is the distance of the ship from the cliff?

50 (a) The speed of sound in air is 340 m/s.
The speed of light in air is 3×10^8 m/s.
In a thunderstorm a lightning flash and a thunderclap are made at the same time.

    (i) Why do you see the lightning flash before you hear the thunderclap?   (1)

    (ii) You see the flash 5 seconds before you hear the thunderclap. Calculate how far away the thunderstorm is.   (3)

(b) A microphone is connected to an oscilloscope. Different musical instruments are played in front of the microphone. The oscilloscope controls remain unaltered. Each instrument is played in the same place each time. The waveforms shown are produced.

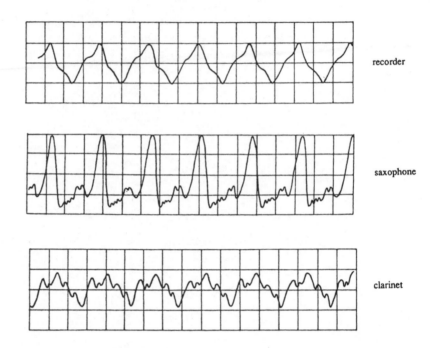

    (i) Which instrument is producing the loudest sound? How can you tell?   (2)

    (ii) How can you tell that all the instruments are producing a note of the same pitch?   (1)

(c) The note made by plucking the strings of a guitar is not very loud. The strings are on a hollow wooden box which makes the sound much louder. Explain this.   (2)

(MEG Central Tier)

51 Bats are small mammals which fly by night and rest during the day. They have poorly developed eyes and very large ears.

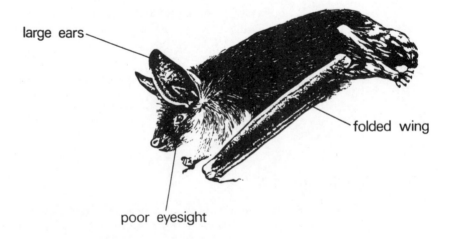

Bats produce bursts of high-pitched sound.

(a) What is meant by high pitch?   (1)

The following diagram shows a trace of the note produced by a bat.

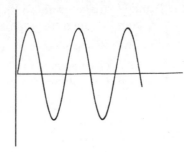

(b) On the axes below, draw a diagram to show the echo that would be received by the bat. (2)

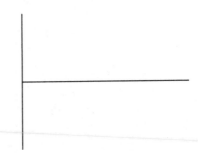

The bat produces the sound by a resonating system.

(c) Explain what is meant by a resonating system. (1)

The frequency of the note given out by the bat is 33 000 Hz.
The sound travels at 330 m/s.

(d) Calculate the wavelength of the sound. (2)

(MEG Nuffield Central Tier)

Chapter 18

52 The diagram shows two bar magnets suspended by similar threads.

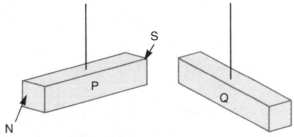

(a) One end of magnet Q is brought near to the S pole of magnet P. The magnets attract. Label the S pole of magnet Q.

(b) If the other end of magnet Q is brought near to the S pole of magnet P, what will happen?

(c) State what you understand by the expression 'magnetic field'.

53 The diagram shows the top view of two bar magnets held on a smooth surface. The magnetic field has been drawn in.

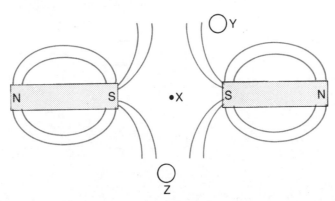

(a) Describe the field at point X.

(b) Y and Z are plotting compasses. Draw an arrow in each circle to show the direction in which the compass needle points.

(c) What will happen to the magnets if they are released?

(d) One of the magnets is turned round as shown below. Draw the magnetic field lines within the dotted boxes.

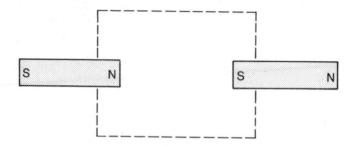

Chapter 20

54 Current and potential difference are two common electrical quantities.

(a) The unit in which current is measured is the .... (1)

(b) The unit in which potential is measured is the .... (1)

(NICCEA Tier Q)

55 A lightbulb and a resistor will both conduct electricity. The graph below shows how the current through each component changes as the potential difference changes.

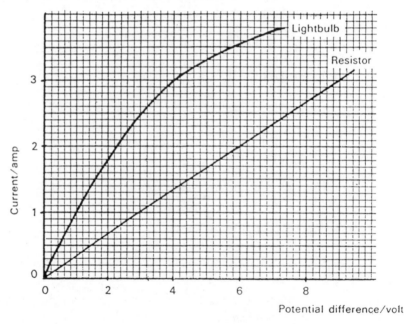

(a) Describe in your own words how the current through the lightbulb changes as the p.d. increases. (2)

(b) Use the graph to calculate the resistance of the resistor. (4)

(c) The bulb and resistor are now connected as shown. The current in the circuit is 2.5 A.

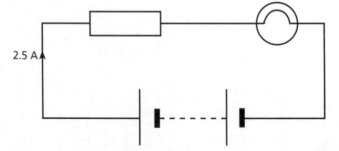

What is the p.d. across

    (i) the resistor?   (2)
    (ii) the bulb?   (2)
    (iii) the battery?   (2)

(d) The resistor and lightbulb are now connected in parallel to a 6 V battery as shown.

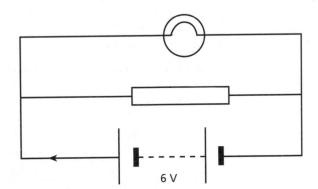

Use the graph to find the current flowing through the battery.

(ULEAC B Paper 2I)

56 A series circuit is set up as shown in the circuit diagram.

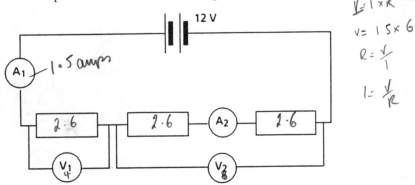

All resistors have the same resistance. Voltmeter V_1 reads 4 V. Ammeter A_1 reads 1.5 A.

(a) What does voltmeter V_2 read?   8   (1)
(b) What does ammeter A_2 read?   1.5   (1)

(NICCEA Tier Q)

57 Alan was asked to set up an experiment to investigate how the current through the filament of a lamp changed with the potential difference across its ends. Alan was provided with connecting wire and five pieces of equipment.

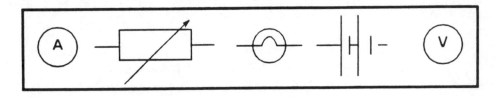

(a)   (i)   Using the symbols above draw a circuit diagram of the apparatus Alan might use in carrying out this investigation.   (3)
      (ii)   Mark with an arrow on your circuit diagram the direction in which electrons flow through the lamp.   (1)

(b)   (i)   Some of the results of this experiment are shown in the table below.

Current I through filament in amperes	0.10	0.25	0.30	0.35
Voltage V across filament in volts	0.10	0.40	0.60	1.00

Plot a graph of current I against voltage V and draw a suitable curve through the data points. (2)

(ii) Use your graph to find the resistance of the filament when the current flowing is 0.3 A. Show clearly how you get your answer. (2)

(iii) In what way, if any, does the resistance of the lamp change as the current through it increases? (1)

(iv) The lamp is at normal brightness when the current flowing through the filament is 0.3 A. Calculate the normal power of the lamp. (2)

(v) Does the lamp obey Ohm's Law? Give a reason for your answer. (3)

(c) (i) When a house is wired it is often necessary to wire a light in such a way that it can be switched on or off from two separate switches. Draw a diagram, in the space below, of a bulb connected to a two-way switch. (2)

(ii) The diagram shows a fused three-pin plug. Label the THREE wires correctly on the diagram. (3)

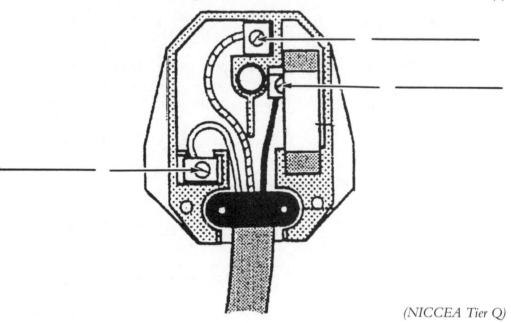

(NICCEA Tier Q)

58 The figure shows a plug wired by a pupil and connected to a hair dryer rated at 100 W, 240 V a.c.

(a) Several **mistakes** have been made. Name **four** of them.

(b) The earth pin on a plug is longer than the other two pins. Explain why.

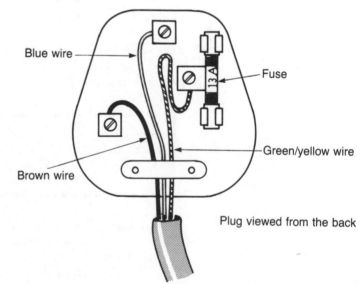

Plug viewed from the back

59 The diagram below shows the structure of an electric storage heater.

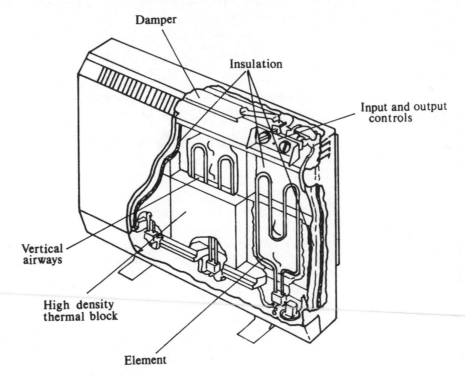

Damper

Insulation

Input and output controls

Vertical airways

High density thermal block

Element

The electrical elements are used to heat the high density thermal blocks overnight. During the day time the heat energy stored is released to the room.

(a)   (i) The power rating of the heater is 3.5 kW. Calculate how much the internal energy of the high density thermal blocks will increase when the electrical supply is on from midnight to 5.00 a.m.
State ONE assumption you have made in making your calculation.

    (ii) The high density thermal blocks have a total mass of 120 kg and a specific heat capacity of 2625 J/kg °C. Calculate the temperature rise of the blocks.

   (iii) Explain why it is necessary in the design of the storage heater to include insulation between the high density blocks and the outer metal casing of the heater.   (9)

(b) The electricity Board charges 0.8p for each kilowatt hour during the period midnight to 5.00 a.m. In the day time they charge 8p for each kilowatt hour.

  (i) Explain why the Electricity Board does this.

  (ii) Calculate the weekly cost of running the storage heater at the night time rate.   (5)

(c) During the day the thermal energy stored in the heater during the night is released into the room.

  (i) Explain how this energy transfer takes place from the storage heater and how the rate of transfer can be controlled.

  (ii) The Electricity Board claims that this method of heating is one hundred percent efficient. Explain what they mean by this and whether the claim is justified.

  (iii) Explain what the drawbacks of this method of heating would be if there were sudden changes in the weather.   (7)

(d) When the Electricity Board connects storage heaters in the home they have a separate circuit. They are not connected to the ring main circuit. Give TWO reasons for this   (3)

(ULEAC A Paper 2I)

60 The information below is taken from a household electricity bill.

tariffs and meter readings			cost per unit	total cost
present	*previous*	*units used*		
10491	08189	2302	5.77 p (day)	£132.83
35952	28739	7213	1.90 p (night)	£137.05

It shows two prices for a unit of electricity. One unit of electricity is 1 kW hour.

(a) Suggest and explain reasons why the Electricity Board sells electricity which is used at night at a cheaper price. (4)

(b) Many householders use electricity during the night to run a 3 kW heater for heating a tank of water.

    (i) Calculate the cost of having this heater on for four hours during the night. Show your working. (2)

    (ii) How much electric current is passing through the heater whilst it is in use? The mains supply to the house is 240 V. Show your working. (3)

(MEG Salters Further Tier)

Chapter 21

61 A student set up the electric motor shown in the diagram.

(a) The motor did not work. What was wrong with it?

(b) Why did this prevent the motor from working?

(c) When the mistake was corrected the motor turned.

    (i) Suggest **three** ways of making the coil turn faster.

    (ii) Suggest **two** ways of making the coil turn the other way.

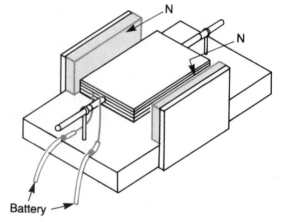

62 The diagram below shows two coil electromagnets. The magnets are attracting each other.

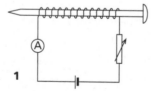
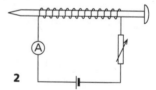

The table below suggests various changes that could be made to the coils or circuits.

action	change in circuit 1	change in circuit 2
A	increase the current in the coil	no change
B	no change	increase the current in the coil
C	increase the current in the coil	increase the current in the coil
D	unwind some of the coils	unwind some of the coils
E	reverse the current in the coil	no change
F	no change	reverse the current in the coil
G	reverse the current in the coil	reverse the current in the coil

(a) List the letters of all of the actions which would make the magnets attract each other more strongly. (2)

(b) List the letters of all the actions which, **if carried out separately**, would make the magnets repel each other. (2)

The diagram shows a moving coil speaker.

(c) The speaker contains a permanent magnet. Draw an arrow on the diagram pointing to the permanent magnet. (1)

(d) Explain how this type of speaker produces sound waves when a varying electric current flows through the coil. (4)

(MEG Salters Further Tier)

Chapter 22

63 The diagram shows a simple generator connected to a lamp. The lamp lights normally when the coil is rotating at its maximum speed.

(a) Describe what happens to the brightness of the lamp as the speed of the coil is increased from zero to its maximum speed.

(b) What would be the effect on the lamp of reducing the number of turns on the coil which is rotating at maximum speed?

(c) What would be the effect on the lamp of increasing the strength of the magnetic field, the coil having its original number of turns and rotating at maximum speed?

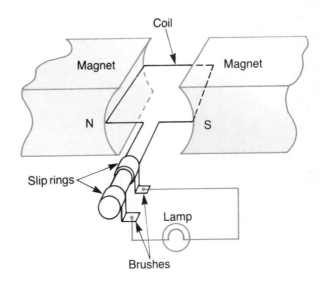

64 (a) The diagram shows an electromagnetic relay.

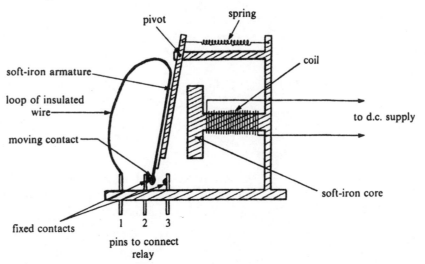

Pins 2 and 3 are connected to the fixed contacts. Pin 1 is connected to the moving contact by the loop of wire.

The diagram shows the relay as it is when there is no current in the coil. A current now flows in the coil. What happens to the core, the soft-iron armature and the contacts? (3)

(b) The diagram below shows a simple step-down transformer.

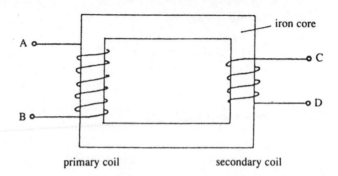

primary coil   secondary coil

    (i) What is the purpose of a step-down transformer? (2)
    (ii) How does a step-up transformer differ from a step-down transformer? (2)

(MEG Central Tier)

65 The diagram shows a simple form of transformer used for stepping down an alternating voltage supply.

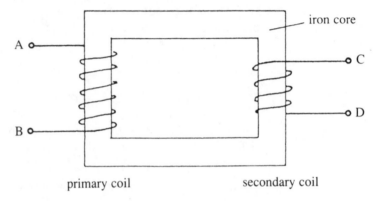

primary coil   secondary coil

(a) By writing about magnetic fields, explain how the transformer works. (3)

(b) A power line supplies electrical energy to a transformer in a factory. The input voltage to the transformer is 11 000 V. The transformer changes this to 415 V for use in the factory. The power input to the transformer is 800 kW.

    (i) Calculate the current in the secondary coil of the transformer. (3)
    What assumptions have you made about the transformer? (1)
    (ii) The power line to the factory is operated at as high a voltage as possible. Explain why this is so. (4)

(MEG Further Tier)

66 Electrical energy is transmitted through the National Grid at very high voltage. Near to each group of consumers, a sub-station has transformers which reduce the voltage to 240 V.

(a) Draw a diagram of a transformer and label it to show the primary and secondary coils, and the core. (4)

(b)   (i) What material is used for making the core of transformers? (1)
    (ii) Explain why concrete is not used for transformer coils. (2)
    (iii) Explain why steel is not used for transformer coils. (1)

(c) The supply cables to a local transformer are at a potential of 11 000 V. The transformer converts this to a local supply voltage of 240 V. If the primary coil of this transformer has 880 turns, how many turns has the secondary coil? Show your working. (2)

(d) In the space below, draw an energy flow arrow diagram to represent the energy changes which take place in the transformer. The diagram should include any unwanted changes which occur. (4)

(MEG Salters Central Tier)

Chapter 23

67 The diagram shows an electron gun in the back of a television set.

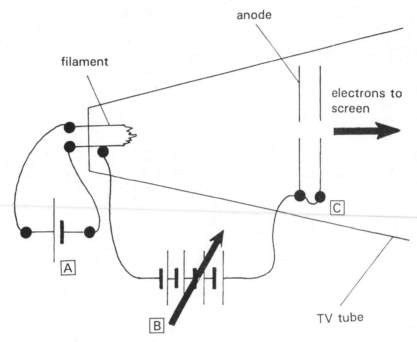

(a) Does it make any difference to the television picture if the battery A is reversed? Explain your answer. (2)

(b) Does it make any difference to the television picture if the battery B is reversed? (2)

(c) Why are there two plates at C each with a small hole? (2)

(d) If you were making a TV what would you label the control at B? Explain your choice. (2)

(MEG Nuffield Central Tier)

68 A light beside the front door of a house is designed so that it will only go on when somebody is standing on the doormat, **and** it is dark. The control unit includes a pressure switch under the mat and a light sensor (which is ON in daylight and OFF at night).

(a) Where should the light sensor be placed so that it does not switch ON when the light comes ON? (1)

(b) The control circuit will need two logic gates, an AND gate and a NOT gate. Part of the circuit diagram is shown below. Complete the diagram to show where the NOT gate should be placed. (1)

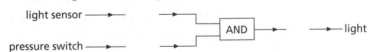

(c) Complete the truth tables to show how each gate works.

(i) AND gate

input 1	input 2	output
OFF	OFF	
OFF	ON	
ON	OFF	
ON	ON	

(ii) NOT gate

input	output
ON	
OFF	

(3)
(MEG Salters Central Tier)

69 The circuit diagram shows how a transistor may be used to operate a switch which makes a light come on when it gets dark.

(a) What happens to the resistance of the light sensitive resistor when it gets dark?

(b) What effect does this change of resistance have on the collector current?

(c) Why is a variable resistor preferred to a fixed resistor at A?

(d) Why is it better to use a relay rather than to insert a bulb directly at B?

(e) What is the purpose of the resistor R_1?

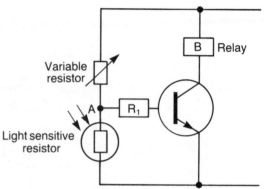

70 A photographer has been having trouble because people open her darkroom door at the wrong moment and 'fog' films she is working on. She has designed the circuit below for a warning light outside the door.

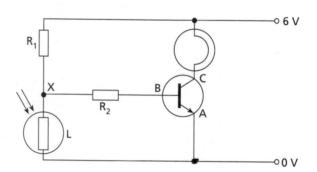

The component L is a light-dependent resistor. In darkness, its resistance is several million ohms. In full light, the resistance falls to only a few ohms.

(a) On the diagram, write the names usually given to the three terminals of the transistor (A, B and C). (3)

(b) To the nearest volt, what is the voltage at the point X
    (i) when the darkroom light is off?
    (ii) when the darkroom light is on? (2)

(c) What will be seen outside the door when the darkroom light is off? (1)

(d) Explain how the circuit could be modified so that it could be adjusted to turn the warning light on at different light levels. (2)

(MEG Salters Central Tier)

Chapter 24

71 A detector shows that the activity of a radioactive sample falls from 160 units to 20 units in 15 minutes. Determine the half-life of the sample, explaining your calculation.

72 The diagram shows nuclear fission of uranium 235 in a nuclear reactor.

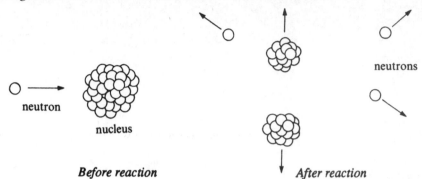

Before reaction   *After reaction*

(a) Describe the process shown in the diagrams. Explain how it can lead to a chain reaction. (5)

(b) After the reactor has been running for a few years the uranium fuel rods in the reactor are removed and taken to Sellafield. There the waste products are separated and put into large cans which are then sealed.
The cans are then kept in water.
Give TWO reasons why the waste products are kept in sealed cans, under water. (2)

(MEG Central Tier)

73 (a) (i) Here is a diagram of a neutral atom. Complete the diagram by writing in the space the FOUR missing labels. (2)

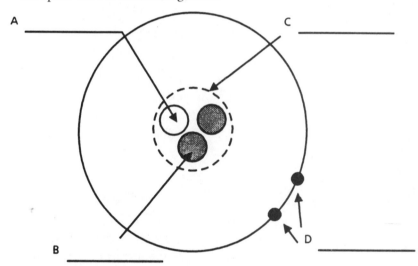

(ii) State ONE way in which the isotopes of an element are similar and ONE way in which they are different. (2)

(iii) The nucleus of one isotope of barium is unstable and disintegrates by emitting a beta particle. Complete the equation below by writing the correct number in each of the boxes (La is the symbol for lanthanum). (4)

$$^{139}_{56}\text{Ba} \rightarrow {}^{\square}_{\square}\text{La} + {}^{\square}_{\square}\beta$$

(iv) From which part of the barium atom does the beta particle come? (1)

(b) When uranium 235 absorbs a neutron it undergoes fission (break up). The equation below shows one way in which this can happen.

$$^{235}_{92}\text{U} + {}^{1}_{0}\text{n} \rightarrow {}^{144}_{56}\text{Ba} + {}^{90}_{36}\text{Kr} + \text{neutrons}$$

(i) How many neutrons are released by this fission? (1)
(ii) In addition to the many particles released in this fission what else is released? (1)

(NICCEA Tier R)

Chapter 25

74 (a) (i) The diagram shows a planet in circular orbit around the Sun. At each position of the planet shown, mark clearly the direction of the force acting on the planet. (1)

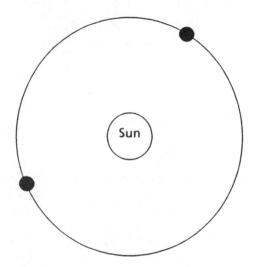

(ii) What causes the force on the planet? (1)

(iii) Scientists believe that our Solar System began as a huge cloud of gas and dust rotating in space. Describe and explain how this resulted in the formation of the Sun and the planets. (4)

(b) (i) Evidence for the spherical model of the Earth comes from many sources, one of which is the position of stars in the sky.

The diagrams show a ship sailing on a flat Earth and a curved Earth. Give TWO differences relating to the stars S1 and S2 and the positions P1 and P2 of the ship that would be noticed for each model. (4)

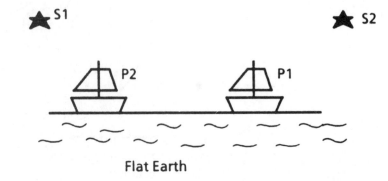

Flat Earth

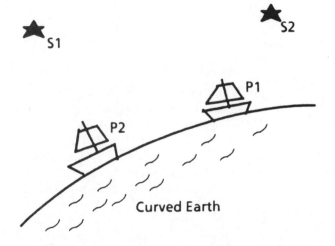

Curved Earth

(ii) The Earth has a layered structure. On the diagram below label the layers indicated by the arrows. (2)

A. _____

B. _____

C. _____

D. _____

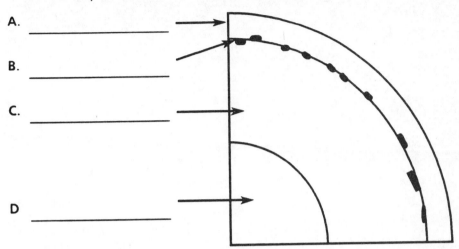

When an earthquake takes place waves are sent out through the Earth and can be detected thousands of kilometres from the place at which the quake occurs. Two types of wave are sent out – P and S.

(iii) Explain how P and S waves differ in the way they are transmitted through the earth. (2)

(iv) The trace below is from a seismometer which detects earthquake waves. Calculate the ratio of the average speed of P waves to those of S waves. The first P wave arrives at the seismometer 7 minutes after the quake. (5)

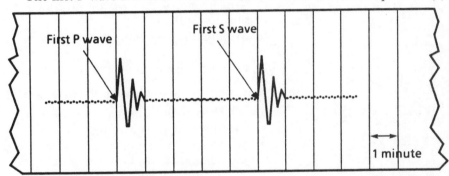

(v) Explain, with the help of the diagram of the Earth below, what is meant by the Shadow Zone in the detection of earthquakes' waves. What does the existence of this zone tell us about the composition of the Earth? (3)

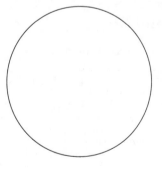

(NICCEA Tier R)

75 The diagram below shows the different air streams (air masses) that can affect the British weather. Use the diagram to help you answer the questions that follow it.

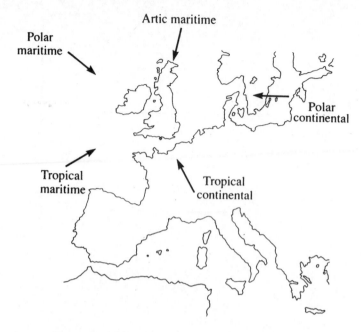

(a) In the summer of 1989, there were long periods of hot, dry weather. People noticed that their cars were often covered with a fine, dry, red dust.

   (i) Which one of the five air streams dominated the weather during the summer of 1989? (1)

   (ii) Mark on the map with a X where the red dust is likely to have come from. (1)

   (iii) How did the red dust get to Britain? (1)

(b) The weather in the south-west of Britain is usually warm and humid (damp).

   (i) Which two airsteams are most likely to bring damp weather to Britain? Give a reason for your answer. (2)

   (ii) Which one of the airstreams gives the south-west of Britain its usual weather conditions? Give a reason for your answer. (3)

(c) Which one of the airstreams would cause the weather conditions described here: *Very dry, cool in summer, very cold in winter?* (1)

(SEG Intermadiate Tier)

Chapter 26

76 Some information about planets in the Solar system is given in the table.

planet	length of day	length of year
Earth	24 hours	365 days
Mars	24 hours 40 min	686 'Earth' days
Venus	2808 hours	225 'Earth' days
X	10 hours	10753 'Earth' days
Y	4224 hours	88 'Earth' days

(a) In terms of the movement of a planet, explain what is meant by
   (i) a day (2)
   (ii) a year (2)

(b) Which of the planets X, or Y, would you expect to be closest to the Sun? Explain your answer. (3)

(c) On each planet, a day is divided into so many hours of darkness, and so many hours of light. Explain why in Summer in Britain it is light for more than 12 hours each day, whereas in Winter it is light for less than 12 hours each day. (3)

(MEG Salters Central Tier)

77 (a) Every object attracts every other object with a force.

Earth   Moon

    (i) What type of force is acting between the Earth and the Moon? (1)
    (ii) What **two** factors does this force depend on? (2)
    (iii) What evidence is there on Earth to show the force of the Moon? (1)

(b) The asteroids can be considered as bits of a planet that fell apart. They orbit between Mars and Jupiter. Use the following data to suggest similar data for these asteroids. Give a brief explanation for your suggestions. (6)

Planet	Relative mass (Earth = 1)	Surface gravity field/N/kg	Distance from Sun/Millions of km	Surface temp. °C
Mercury	0.05	3.6	58.0	350
Venus	0.81	0.87	107.5	460
Earth	1.0	9.8	149.6	20
Mars	0.11	3.7	228	−23
Jupiter	318.0	25.9	778	−120
Saturn	95.0	11.3	1427	−180
Uranus	14.0	10.4	2870	−210
Neptune	17.5	14.0	4497	−220
Pluto	0.003	–	5900	−230

(SEG Higher Tier)

Answers to short answer and structured questions

1 (a) (i) OA, BC   (ii) AB, DE   (iii) CD, 10 m/s

    (b) E
    (c) (i) OA, $a = 15/20 = 0.75$ m/s^2
         or BC, $a = 5/10 = 0.5$ m/s^2
      (ii) AB, $a = 10/10 = 1.0$ m/s^2
         or DE, $a = 10/10 = 1.0$ m/s^2
      (iii) Distance travelled in AB = area under graph
$$= ½ (10 \times 10) + (5 \times 10)$$
$$= 100 \text{ m}$$

    (d) (i) Constant or uniform
      (ii) Speed = slope of graph $= \dfrac{800}{50} = 16$ m/s

2 (a) 30 m/s   (b) travelling at constant speed
(c) decelerating uniformly   (d) B
(e) The train slows down at a greater rate than it speeds up.
(f) 750 m

3 (a) (i) $a = \dfrac{27 - 0}{5.4 - 1.2} = 6.4 \text{ m/s}^2$

(ii) distance travelled = area under curve
$$= \frac{(5.4 + 1.2) \times 27}{2}$$
$$= 89 \text{ m}$$

(allow methods using constant acceleration formulae)

(b) *Answers should include use of correct technical language. 1 mark each for 4 relevant points: e.g.:*
when car brakes, unbelted child does not slow down
when she hits seat back she has large deceleration
large acceleration requires a large force
large force may cause injury
if seat belt worn she slows down more gradually
smaller force acts to slow her down

4 (a) (i) distance equals area under graph
$$= 0.5 \times 125 \times 25$$
$$= 1562.5 \text{ m}$$

(ii) acceleration = slope
$125/25 = 5 \text{ m/s}^2$

(b) (i) using $s = ut + \tfrac{1}{2}at^2$
$10\,000 = 0.5 \times 10 \times t^2$
$\dfrac{10\,000}{5} = t^2$
$t = 44.7$ s

(ii) distance $= 200 \times 44.7 = 8940$ m

(iii) $v^2 = u^2 + 2as$
$v^2 = 0 + 2 \times 10 \times 10\,000$
$= 200\,000$
$v = 447.2$ m/s

(iv) 200 m/s

(c) parabolic shape, horizontal and vertical axes labelled, correct vertical height and horizontal distance marked

5 (a) 6 s   (b) 6 s   (c) 240 m

6 (a) A air resistance
B weight
(b) (i) terminal velocity
(ii) balanced
(c) (i) 2 s (C)
(ii) 20 m/s
(iii) distance = speed × time
$= 10$ m/s × 2 s
$= 20$ m

7 (a) 25 kg   (b) 42.5 N

8 (a) (i) the gravitational force between the two
(ii) the tension in the string
(iii) the frictional force between the tyre and the road
(b) inwards

9 (a) (i) General statement:
Conservation of momentum states that, when two objects interact, their total momentum remains constant, providing no external force is acting on them.

Specific statement:
The gain in momentum of the rocket is equal and opposite to the momentum of the ejected hot gases.

(ii) $(m \times v)$ spaceship $+ (m \times v)$ gases $= 0$
$(25\,000 \times v) + (10 \times 10\,000) = 0$
$v = -4$ m/s (increase in velocity)

(b) (i) momentum $= m \times v$
$= 2100 \times 15 = 31500$ kg m/s

(ii) $(m \times v)$ car $= (m \times v)$ van at collision
$900 \times v = 31500$
$v = 35$ m/s
This shows that the car was speeding.
25 m/s is the speed limit.

10 6 m/s in the opposite direction to that in which the girl moves.

11 0.2 m/s

12 (a) 400 N. As the car is travelling at a constant speed, there is no total force acting on it. Thus the force exerted by the tow rope must be equal and opposite to the force of friction.

(b) The extra force which accelerates the car is $2000 - 400 = 1600$ N

Use $F = ma$ to calculate $a = \dfrac{1600}{1200} = 1.33$ m/s^2.

13 (a) 6.4 J   (b) 6.4 J   (c) 8 m/s   (d) 10 m/s^2 (e) 2 N

14 (a) 0.8 s

(b) (i) $\frac{1}{2} \times 1140 \times 400 = 228\,000$ J
(ii) 228 000 J
(iii) $Fs = 228\,000$
$F = 6000$ N
(iv) Converted to heat/thermal energy

(c) The car is turning to the right. The passengers tend to go on in a straight line. *Relative to the car* the passengers feel they are being forced outwards. The car has to exert an inward force on the passengers to get them round the corner.

(d) The force exerted on any object is equal to its rate of change of momentum

$$F = \frac{mv - mu}{t}$$

The crumple zones increase the time it takes to stop the car and its passengers, thus *decreasing* the force acting on them.

15 (a) (i) falling towards trampoline with uniform acceleration
(ii) hitting trampoline, non-uniform deceleration

(b) (i) A/E
(ii) 1. kinetic energy of gymnast changing to elastic potential energy in trampoline
2. elastic potential energy in trampoline changing to kinetic energy of gymnast
3. kinetic energy of gymnast changing to gravitational potential energy

(c) (i) K.E. $= \frac{1}{2} mv^2$
$= \frac{1}{2} \times 60 \times 10^2$
$= 3000$ J

(ii) P.E. $= mgh$
$= 60 \times 10 \times 5$
$= 3000$ J
same

16 (i) it is increasing
(ii) gravitational pull of Moon less
not as much work to do to escape
also Earth's field will return craft
(iii) astronaut + spacecraft in free-fall
no reaction possible with floor of craft
no sensation of weight

17 (a) (i) 32 J   (ii) 32 J   (iii) 4 W   (b) (i) 24.5 J   (ii) 7 m/s

18 (a) Work done = force × distance moved (in direction of force)
$$= 500 \text{ N} \times 25 \text{ m/s} \times 20 \text{ s}$$
$$= 250\ 000 \text{ J}$$
   (b) Efficiency = useful output energy/ total input energy
$$= 250\ 000\ /\ 1\ 000\ 000 \times 100\%$$
$$= 25\ \%\ (\text{or } 0.25)$$

19 (a)   (i) Any four:
      Reserves are estimated
      quantity used each year can vary
      environmental considerations
      reserves depleted
      more use of large reserves
      due to cost etc.
    (ii) Oil reaching low reserves
      Use of other fuels/renewable sources of energy
   (iii) Economic – large capital investment,
      however, electricity 'cheap' to produce
      Environmental – no greenhouse gases/acid rain,
      ash (waste problem)
      Social – more use of electrical power in future, 'clean'
      atmosphere
   (b)   (i) 400 × 10 = 4000 N
     (ii) E(change) = 4000 × 500 = 2 000 000 J or 2 MJ
    (iii) 2 MJ per second = 2 MW
    (iv) watts = volts × amps (power = VI)
$$\text{current } I = \frac{2\ 000\ 000}{20\ 000} = 100 \text{ A}$$
     (v) More power used returning water to upper reservoir
      Hence, *not* efficient/economic

20 (a) A vector quantity has direction as well as size
     A scalar quantity has size only
   (b) Vector – e.g. momentum, force, velocity. Scalar – e.g. mass, volume.

21 R = 50 N
    S = 40 N

22 3 N

23 (a) 20 N   (b) 27.5 N upwards

24 (a)

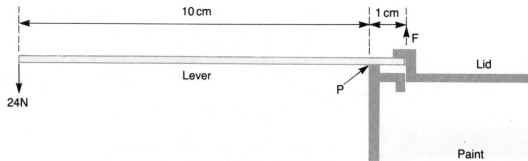

   (b) 2.4 Nm or 240 Ncm   (c) 240 N (d) 264 N
   (e) Increase the size of the force applied to the end of the lever or increase the
     length.

25 (a) 24 cm^2 (b) 8 cm^3 (c) 64 g

26 (a) 100 000 N   (b) 100 000 N   (c) 1000 Pa (N/m^2)   (d) 25 000 N

27 (i) arrow on diagram near slave cylinder pointing UPWARDS
   (ii) the liquid is not compressible and transmits pressure from master cylinder to
     slave cylinder

(iii) Take moments about pivot
$$25 \times 100 = 5 \times F$$
$$F = 500 \text{ N}$$
(iv) $P = F/A$
$$= 300/20$$
$$= 15 \text{ N/cm}^2$$
$$= 15 \times 10\ 000 \text{ N/m}^2$$
$$= 150\ 000 \text{ Pascals}$$
(v) $F = P \times A$
$$= 15 \times 2$$
$$= 30 \text{ N}$$

28 (a) 30 N   (b) N/m   (c) 0.04 g/cm^3

29 (a) The springs represent the forces between molecules.
(b) When a solid is heated the molecules vibrate about their average position with greater amplitude. The spheres in the model should be made to vibrate with greater amplitude.
(c) In a liquid the molecules move throughout the liquid. In a solid molecules stay in the same average position.
(d) Energy is needed to separate the molecules, i.e. to overcome the bonding forces

30 (a) As a solid is heated the molecules vibrate with greater amplitude and the average distance between neighbouring molecules increases slightly. Thus the solid becomes larger.
(b) When the rivets cool they contract and the two plates are squeezed together between the ends of each rivet.
(c)

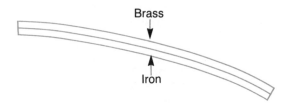

Brass

Iron

31 (a)   (i) to allow for expansion/contraction
(ii) road would crumple
(b)   (i) get smaller
(ii) get bigger
(c)   (i) increases
(ii) remains the same
(iii) increases
(iv) remains the same

32 (a) points lie (almost) on a straight line through the origin hence quantities plotted are directly proportional
(b) Law applies within the range of pressures measured subject to experimental errors
(c) best fit line drawn by candidate
$1/V = 3400$ (*or as read from candidate's line*)
$V = 2.9 \times 10^{-4} \text{ m}^3$
(d)   (i) straight line through the origin drawn twice as steep as previous line
(ii) Boyle's law applies doubling temperature doubles pressure

33 (a) 1.5 litres   (b) 0.67 atmospheres

34 (i) less than 30°C   (ii) greater than 30°C

35 (a) conduction   (b) convection   (c) radiation

36 (a) Rods of same length
Rods of same cross-sectional area
Heat conducts through rods and melts wax
Copper drops first as is best conductor
(b) A – Arrow UP
B – Arrow DOWN
C – Arrow DOWN
Convection
To minimise heat loss by conduction from hot water through pipe
(c) Any ONE of
windows (double glazing)
door (draughts)
floor (carpets)
or acceptable alternatives

37 (a) (i) Any two from
Same distance from heater
Same volume/mass of water in each
Same metal for each can
(ii) Can Y
Dull surfaces are better absorbers of radiant heat.
(b) Roof: Glass fibre matting   Conduction
Floor: Carpets   Conduction
Walls: Polystyrene foam   Conduction

38 (a) The disturbance which causes the wave is in the same direction
as the wave travels.
(b) Transverse: water, radio, light.   Longitudinal: sound

39 (i) Cork moves up and down.
(ii) Waves transport energy.
(iii) Amplitude = 5 cm
Frequency = 0.5 Hz
(iv) Velocity   = frequency × wavelength
                 = 0.5 × 0.8
                 = 0.4 m/s

40 (a) Smaller   (b) The filament is inverted

41 (a), (b), (c)

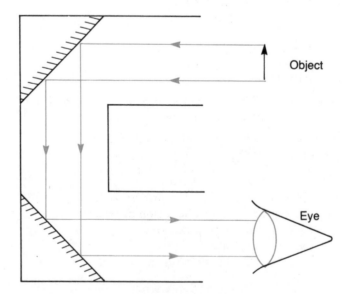

(d) It gives a narrow angle of view.

42 (a) (i) refraction   (ii) critical angle
(b) (i) The speed of light increases as it goes from glass to air.
(ii) The ray hits the surface at more than the critical angle and is reflected.

43 (a) lens, retina and nerve
　(b) (i) pupil　(ii) iris　(iii) lens　(iv) retina
　　(v) optic nerve
　(c) (i) long sight　(ii) Draw a convex lens

44 thin or weak, behind, converging, on

45 long, in front of, diverging, on

46 (a) The spreading could be increased by making the slit narrower.
　(b) The wavelength remains the same.
　(c) The diffraction (spreading out) would be greater.

47 (a) The wave nature of light (diffraction, interference).
　(b)　(i) bright　(ii) dark bands
　(c)　(i) bright　(ii) bright　(iii) dark
　(d) The fringe separation would become less (fringes closer together).
　(e) The fringe separation would become greater (fringes further apart).

48 (a)　wavelength = speed/frequency
$$= \frac{3 \times 10^8}{1.2 \times 10^6} = 250$$
　　distance = 40 000
$$\text{no. of waves} = \frac{40\ 000}{250} = 160$$
　(b) each wave has travelled same distance/taken same time/waves arrive in phase
　　amplitudes add/constructive interference occurs
　　(*might be shown by diagram*)
　(c) waves from P and Q have travelled different distances.
　　PX exceeds XQ by half a wavelength/ship has moved quarter wavelength
　(d) zero (OR very small amplitude)
　　interference causes cancellation/destructive interference
　(e) See Unit 16.4.
　(f) transverse vibrations can occur in particular plane
　　(*may be shown in a diagram*)

49 750 m

50 (a)　(i) Light travels faster than sound.
　　(ii) distance = speed × time
　　　distance = 340 m/s × 5 s
　　　　= 1700 m
　(b)　(i) saxophone
　　　The wave has the largest amplitude.
　　(ii) All patterns repeat every 2.5 squares.
　(c) The strings cause the box to vibrate.
　　The box causes the air to vibrate (more effectively than the strings).

51 (a) high frequency
　(b) draw same frequency, but smaller amplitude
　(c) one that oscillates best at a single frequency
　(d) wavelength = speed/frequency = 330/33000 m = 1 cm

52 (a) The S pole of magnet Q is the furthest one from the magnet P.
　(b) They will repel.　(c) The region in which magnetic forces are experienced.

53 (a) There is no field at X. It is a neutral point.
(b)

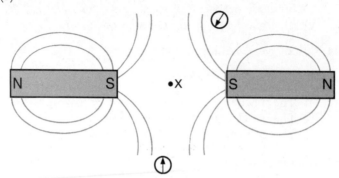

(c) They will move further apart.
(d)

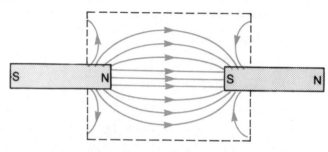

54 (a) Amp (b) Volt

55 (a) current increases rapidly at first then more slowly
(b) $V = IR$
reading of p.d. from resistor line on graph (e.g. 6 volts)
reading of corresponding current value (e.g. 2 amps)
divide to give 3 ohms
(c) (i) From graph: 7.4 V (ii) 3 V (iii) 10.4 V
(d) 2 amp + 3.5 amp = 5.5 amp

56 (a) 8 V (b) 1.5 A

57 (a) (i) Ammeter in series
Voltmeter in parallel with lamp
Battery and resistor in series
(ii) Electrons travel from negative to positive terminal
(b) (i) Points plotted correctly
Smooth curve
(ii) Values from graph for substitution in $V = IR$
Answer: 2 Ω (unit needed)
(iii) Resistance increases
(iv) $P = V \times I$
$= 0.60 \times 0.30$
$= 0.18$ W
(v) No
graph is not a straight line
(c) (i)

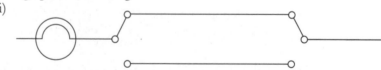

(ii) Neutral on left, earth at top, live on right (going into fuse)

58 (a) Four of the following:
1 The brown wire is connected to the neutral terminal. It should be connected to the live one.
2 The blue wire is connected to earth. It should be connected to the neutral terminal.

3　The green/yellow wire is connected to the live terminal. It should be connected to earth.

4　The outside cable insulation has been cut back too far, so that the cable is not properly clamped by the clench and all the strain comes on the terminals.

5　There is a sharp kink in the green/yellow wire.

(b) When the plug is pushed into a socket, the longer earth pin opens gates to the live and neutral connections.

59 (a)　(i)　$3500 \times 5 \times 60 \times 60 = 63$ MJ
　　　　assumption: all heat energy goes to the blocks

　　　(ii)　$(63 \times 10^6)/(2625 \times 120)$
　　　　　　$= 200°C$

　　　(iii)　to prevent burning oneself on the metal cover
　　　　　　(not to stop heat loss)

(b)　(i)　little demand for electricity at night
　　　　　but it cannot be stored
　　　　　encouraged to use surplus by making it cheaper
　　　　　(not that it is cheaper to produce at night)

　　　(ii)　$3.5 \times 5 \times 7 \times 0.8 = 98$ p

(c)　(i)　vertical airways to allow convection to take place
　　　　　damper to block vents and control rate of transfer

　　　(ii)　Yes. All electrical energy ends up as heat energy in the room

　　　(iii)　Cannot increase/decrease heat output to accommodate large temperature changes. Only good for general background heating.

(d)　1　need a separate meter for monitoring amount of energy used
　　　2　fuse rating needs to be much higher than normal

60 (a)　generators run most efficiently at steady load
　　　load fluctuates, high in day, low at night
　　　differential price helps spread demand
　　　thus plant can keep operating near optimum load

(b)　(i)　number. of units used　$=$ power $\times$ time
　　　　　　　　　　　　　　　$= 3 \times 4$ kWh
　　　　　　　　　　　　　　　$= 12$ kWh
　　　　cost $= 12 \times 1.90$ per unit $= 22.8$ pence

　　　(ii)　power $=$ p.d. $\times$ current
　　　　　　$3000 = 240 \times I$
　　　　　　$I = \dfrac{3000}{240} = 12.5$ amps

61 (a)　The two magnets both have the same pole facing inwards.

(b)　This means that there is a very weak magnetic field between the magnets, and therefore very little force on the sides of the coil.

(c)　(i)　Stronger magnets, more turns on the coil, a larger current.

　　　(ii)　Interchange the two magnets, reverse the direction of current flow.

62 (a)　A, B, C,

(b)　E, F

(c)　See Unit 21.3

(d)　varying electric current gives varying magnetic field
　　　movement of diaphragm as it is attracted to magnet
　　　movement of air layer next to diaphragm
　　　movement of sound waves through air

63 (a)　The lamp will be out or very dim for slow speeds. As the speed increases the brightness of the lamp will increase until it reaches its normal brightness when the coil is rotating at its maximum speed.

(b)　The lamp would become less bright.

(c)　The lamp would become brighter.

64 (a)　CORE becomes magnetized/becomes an electromagnet
　　　SOFT-IRON ARMATURE is attracted to the core/becomes magnetized
　　　CONTACTS The moving contact moves from 2 to 3

(b) (i) To decrease alternating voltage
    (ii) A step-up transformer has more turns on the secondary than on the primary.
    A step-down has fewer turns on the secondary.

65 (a) primary current produces a magnetic field in iron
    magnetic field passes through secondary coil
    as this magnetic field changes it induces a current in secondary coil

(b) (i) power out = power in
$$415 \times I = 800\,000$$
$$I = 1930 \text{ A}$$
    assumed 100% efficiency

    (ii) for high efficiency/to reduce energy loss
    high voltage means low current, for given power
    low current means low heating effect
    as heating effect proportional to I^2

66 (a) See Unit 22.4
(b) (i) soft iron
    (ii) non-magnetic
    would not provide necessary magnetic coupling between coils
    (iii) permanently magnetized/shows hysteresis

(c) $\dfrac{V_2}{V_1} = \dfrac{N_2}{N_1}$ $\dfrac{240}{11\,000} = \dfrac{N}{880}$
    $N = 19.2$

(d)

heat in primary	heat in core	heat in secondary
↗	↗	↗
electrical energy in primary ⟶	magnetic energy in core ⟶	electrical energy in secondary

67 (a) No, heating effect only important
(b) Yes, changes direction of force on electrons so they do not reach the cathode
(c) allow electrons through in thin stream
(d) brightness, controls speed/energy of electrons

68 (a) on top of the light shade (or other place where light does not shine on it)
(b) in series with the light sensor
(c) (i) outputs are: OFF, OFF, OFF, ON
    (ii) outputs are: OFF, ON

69 (a) The resistance increases.
(b) The collector current increases.
(c) The variable resistor is used to alter the potential of point A. If the potential of A increases, the base current increases. This then increases the collector current.
(d) The relay requires less current to operate it than the bulb does to make it bright.
(e) Resistor R_1 limits the current through the base of the transistor and prevents damage.

70 (a) A is the emitter
    B is the base
    C is the collector
(b) (i) 5 V   (ii) 0 V
(c) The lamp will be lit.
(d) A variable resistor could be used in place of the fixed resistor R_1.

71 5 minutes. The activity falls to one-eighth of its original value. Thus three half-lives have elapsed in 15 minutes.

72 (a) Any **three** of the following:
    the nucleus absorbs a neutron;
    the nucleus splits;
    neutrons are released;

the parts fly apart at high speed;
gamma radiation is emitted.
Neutrons react with further uranium nuclei.
The process repeats.

(b) Any **two** of the following:
Water absorbs radiation from the waste.
Water keeps the cans cool.
The sealed cans prevent leakage of waste.
The radiation hazard is reduced.
The half–lives of the fission products are very long.
The metal cans absorb some radiation.

73 (a) (i) A = neutron   B = proton   C = nucleus   D = electrons
      (ii) Same number of protons
           Different number of neutrons
      (iii)

$$^{139}_{56}Ba \rightarrow \; ^{139}_{57}La + \; ^{0}_{-1}\beta$$

      (iv) The nucleus
   (b) (i) Two
      (ii) Energy

74 (a) (i) In both cases arrow from planet to Sun
      (ii) The gravitational attraction of the Sun
      (iii) The gas cloud contracts under gravitational forces.
            Most of the mass is concentrated at centre forming the Sun.
            Smaller concentrations form planets.
   (b) (i) Flat Earth – stars S1 and S2 always above horizon
                     stars always at same angle to horizon
            Curved Earth – S2 drops below horizon
                     S1, the angle to horizon increases
      (ii) A = atmosphere   B = crust   C = mantle   D = core
      (iii) P waves longitudinal, material oscillates in same plane as wave direction.
            S waves transverse, material oscillates at right angles to plane.
      (iv) D = distance to quake
            7 minutes = time for P waves to arrive
            speed of P waves = D/7
            7 + 5 = time for S waves to arrive
            speed of S waves = D/12
            Ratio = 12/7
      (v) Shadow zone – A region where P or S waves are NOT detected.

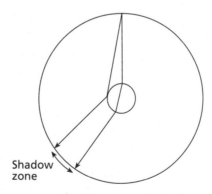

            Evidence for the core/mantle structure

75 (a) (i) tropical continental
      (ii) X at North Africa/Southern Europe
      (iii) picked up and carried by air mass
   (b) (i) polar maritime
            arctic maritime
            tropical maritime (any two)
            all pass over the sea

(ii) tropical maritime
air is wet and warm
(c) polar continental

76 (a)　(i)　one complete revolution of the planet about its own axis
(ii)　one complete orbit of the planet about the Sun

(b)　Y
shorter year
smaller orbits take less time/general pattern is greater distance, greater time

(c)　Earth's axis tilted toward Sun in Summer
away from Sun in Winter

77 (a)　(i)　gravitational
(ii)　mass of objects
distance apart
(iii)　tides

(b)　Could suggest more like Mars if closer to Mars than Jupiter or vice versa.
Suggest a value (range of values between those for Mars and Jupiter) for distance from Sun.
Surface temperature. NOTE must be negative.
Total relative mass (not relative mass) for the asteroids as the parent planet has broken into pieces.
Impossible to give a figure for 'surface gravity' as depends on the mass/size of each asteroid.

Index